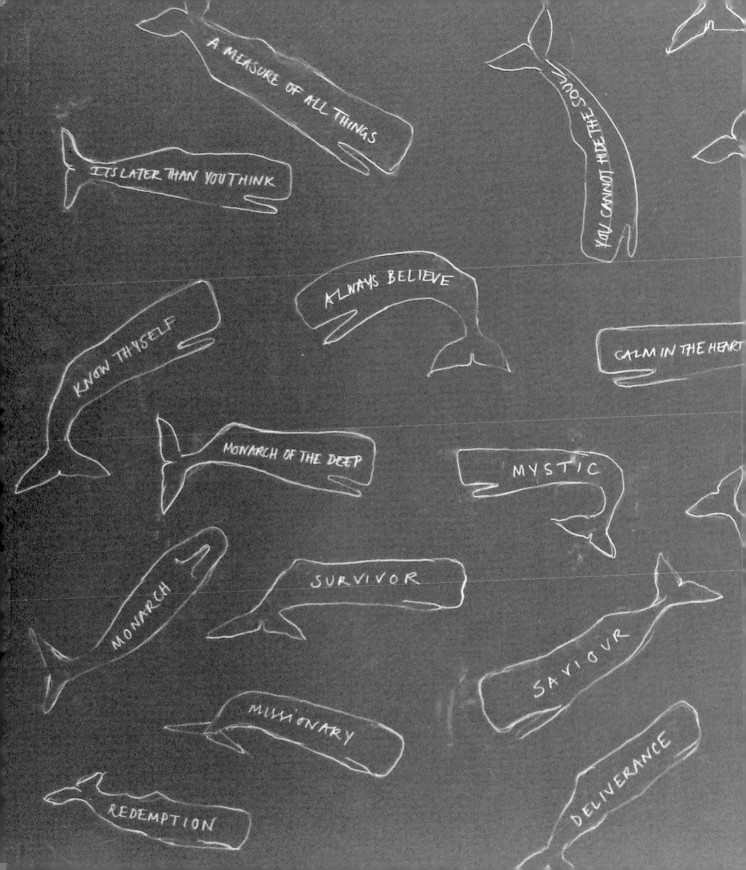

Dominion A Whale Symposium

Kindly donated by

Angela Cockayne

Dominion A Whale Symposium

Angela Cockayne & Philip Hoare

Bath Spa University & Plymouth University

Bath School of Art & Design
Wunderkammer Press
MMXII

First published in 2012:
Wunderkammer Press
Bath School of Art and Design
Bath Spa University
Sion Hill
Bath BA1 5SF

Printed in the United Kingdom

ISBN 978 0 9566462 4 8 [paperback]

Dominion: A Whale Symposium
Angela Cockayne, Philip Hoare

Designed by Matthew Robertson

Cover image © Andrew Sutton

Philip Hoare is supported by The Leverhulme Trust

[RIGHT] *Ahab's Brides*. 2007. Plaster, bridal lace.

In Token

Of Our Admiration For His Genius

This Book Is Inscribed

TO

HERMAN MELVILLE

All men are born with halters round their necks;
but it is only when caught in the swift, sudden turn
of death, that mortals realise the silent, subtle,
ever present perils in life.

— Herman Melville

12–13

CONTENTS

There is no dominion, in blood, in bone, in ash.

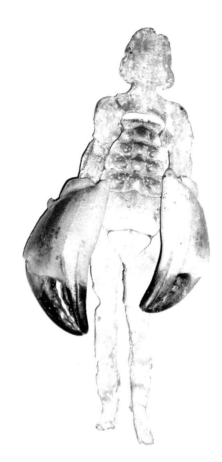

PREFACE
Sarah Chapman

The Peninsula Arts Whale Festival was inspired by both the *Dominion* exhibition, which featured artwork by Angela Cockayne showcased in the Peninsula Arts Gallery, University of Plymouth, January–March 2011, and Philip Hoare's extraordinary, multi-faceted book *Leviathan or, The Whale*. As the curator for the gallery I was fascinated and drawn into the multi-disciplinary approach that both Cockayne and Hoare deploy within their respective mediums. Hoare's text is a sublime inter-disciplinary study of our changing relationship with the magnificent animal that is the whale. He authoritatively brings together science, history, art and literature, weaving a powerful and compelling nar-rative, which explores how the whale has shifted from an economic necessity, driving forward industrial change, to becoming a powerful emblem of the environment.

Peninsula Arts, Plymouth 2011

Similarly Angela Cockayne embraces a multi-disciplinary approach within her art. Often alluding to prevailing concerns as to the relation-ship between the environment and ourselves, her work can perhaps be interpreted as a modern parable for our times. Working collabora-tively with Hoare in a video performance piece also entitled *Dominion*, Cockayne incorporates her sculptures along with costume, music and sound to explore the cultural legacy of the whale. Using the whale as a primary motif throughout the exhibition, Cockayne collects found objects, flotsam and jetsam washed up on beaches, which are then melded together with wax sculpture. The resultant work is both capti-vating and disturbing, half animal, half industrial product, suggestive of either an imaginative primordial past, such as in the immobile fledglings of *Surf & Turf*, or, as in *Cold Feet*, hinting at a possible alterna-tive course of evolution, where the whale does not return to the sea, rather it remains a land-based animal encased entirely in fur. Equally, however, the work proffers a cautionary tale, forewarning us of a pos-sible apocalyptic future, where flesh mutates with human waste such as in the sculptures *Believe it can be Done* or *Sharkfin Cola*.

As in Hoare's *Leviathan or, The Whale*, Cockayne takes inspiration from the great nineteenth-century novel *Moby-Dick* by Herman Meville and often interlaces quotes taken directly from the book such as 'No suicides permitted here' and 'Beware yourself', mixing word with visual analogy and metaphor to both describe, and to disturb, our understanding and relationship to the natural environment. Cockayne also makes visual reference to how the whale has quite literally broadened our very understanding of ourselves and our world, in works such as *Specksynder* (a wax sculpture which incorporates human hair) she questions how, even with current scientific understanding, the whale surpasses our inventions and is able to dive deeper than modern submarines. Likewise, *Hubwhale*, a wax sculpture that is suspended from the ceiling, reminds us that the Hubble telescope, whilst continually extending our understanding of our place within the universe, is in fact lubricated by sperm whale oil.

The exhibition title *Dominion*, with its claims to power and sovereignty, invites us to question our authority over the natural world, yet the exhibition avoids becoming a simple ecological allegory for our times; rather Cockayne seems to both relish and celebrate the very human need to order, to classify and to understand. Bordering on the obsessional, Cockayne herself becomes the collector, bringing together disparate objects such as a typewriter with antique porcelain crowns in place of letters and keys (*Suckle*) or a narwhal tooth (*Museum of Extinction*) in order to present another imaginary worldview.

The aim of the Whale Festival was to both capture and build on the interdisciplinary model as personified by Cockayne and Hoare's work. By bringing together artists, scientists, writers, musicians and poets, whose scholarship and practice had been inspired by the whale, the event encouraged a vivid and productive dialogue between and across disciplines. Although experts were speaking from within their disciplines, often the content resonated with delegates from other subject areas. Key philosophical themes emerged during discussions, concerning the nature of knowledge, and fundamental questions as to how culture is constructed and experienced were raised.

As a public arts programme, operating from within the University of Plymouth, Peninsula Arts has a particular interest in engaging with art practices that interface with scientific and research concerns. One of our key aims is to provide an accessible yet critical programme of events to a new public, where research ideas can be illuminated and interpreted outside specific academic contexts. The success of the Whale

Festival has encouraged us to seek further art/science collaborations in the future, to hopefully provide further platforms for open-ended exchange and reflection as to what motivates and underpins academic research enquiry.

I wish to thank the University of Plymouth, Bath Spa University and in particular the Marine Institute for their generous support and expert advice. Thanks also to Professor Stephen Sterling from the Centre for Sustainable Futures who commissioned a new artwork by Angela Cockayne, *Dead Men Don't Bite*, a fourteen-foot boat of bones, made from biodegradable UV resin.

Dominion 2009, DVD film still, Angela Cockayne & Philip Hoare

OIL
LUBRICANT
PAINT
VARNISH
INK
OINTMENT
DETERGENT
LEATHER FOOD
MARGARINE
VITAMIN A
SHOE SOLES
SHOELACES
CANDLES
CORSETS
SCRIMSHAW
LIPSTICK
COSMETICS
INSULIN
MEDICINE
BRAKE FLUID
ICE-CREAM
SOAP
FERTILISER
CRAYONS
PET FOOD
WHALE MEAT
TYPEWRITER RIBBON
HAIRBRUSHES
DOMINOES
TENNIS RACQUET STRINGS
FILM GLAZE
WATCH OIL
NASA OIL
CORONATION OIL
MUSEUM EXHIBIT
OR
DOWRY

SALT
HAIR
PEWTER ORGAN PIPES
CRUSTACEAN SHELLS
LACE
PLASTER
WAX
CASSOCK
WHITE COTTON DRESS
TOPE FINS
COKE BOTTLE
CHAMPAGNE BOTTLE
HAIR GRIPS
TYPEWRITER
PORCELAIN TEETH
DENTURE WAX
WHALE VERTEBRAE
GOLDFISH
ANVIL
CASTS OF
PIGS TROTTER, SQUID, PIG HEART
NARWHAL TUSKS
GOLD
WOOD
BARREL
DOGFISH SKINS
SHEEP BONES
GANNET
PITH HELMET
CLAY PIPES
SNOOKER BALLS
TAMPON APPLICATORS
GLASS EYES
PLASTIC WHITE SHOVEL
STRING
UV ECO RESIN

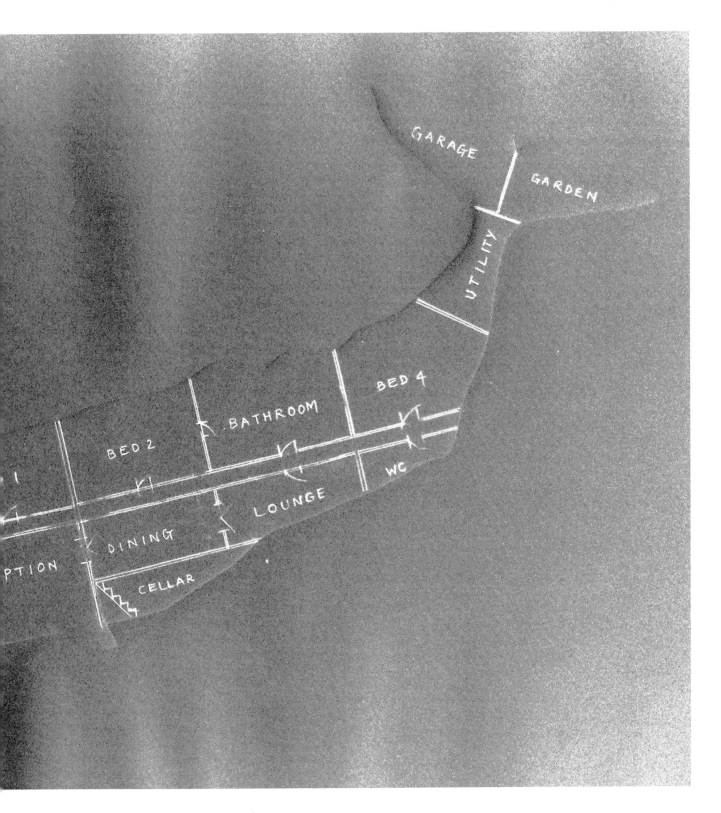

GARAGE

GARDEN

UTILITY

BED 4

BATHROOM

BED 2

WC

LOUNGE

DINING

PTION

CELLAR

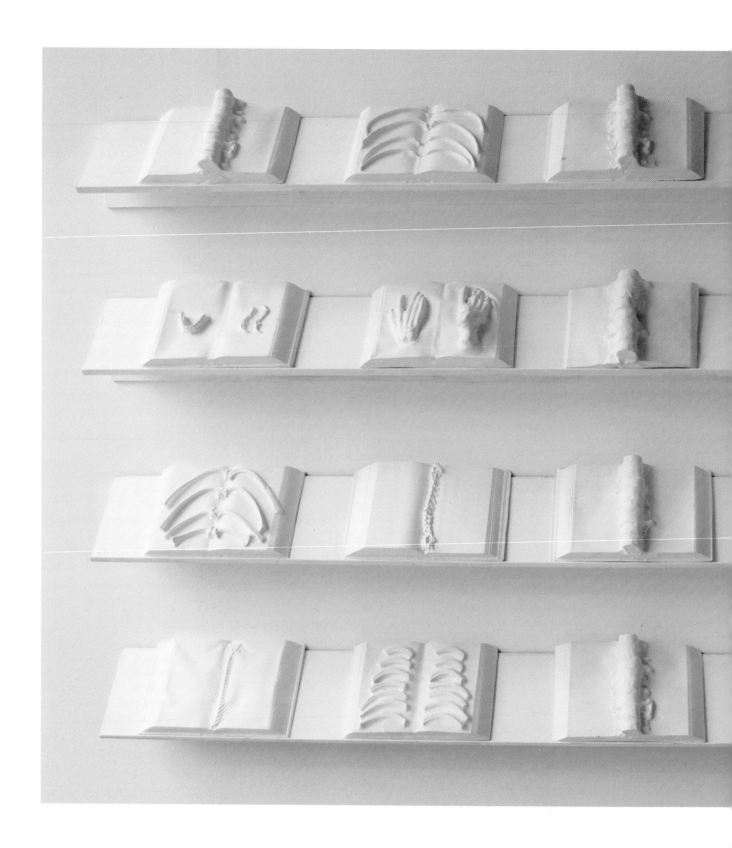

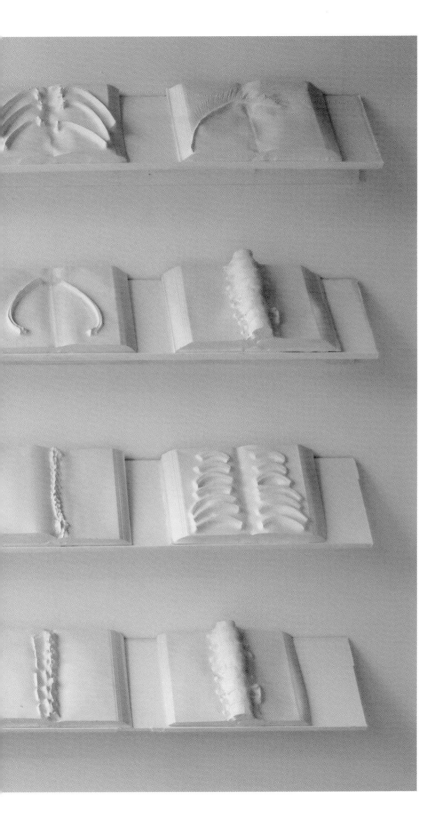

Bone Texts. 2010–11. Plaster.

Above all things it was the whiteness of the whale which appalled me.

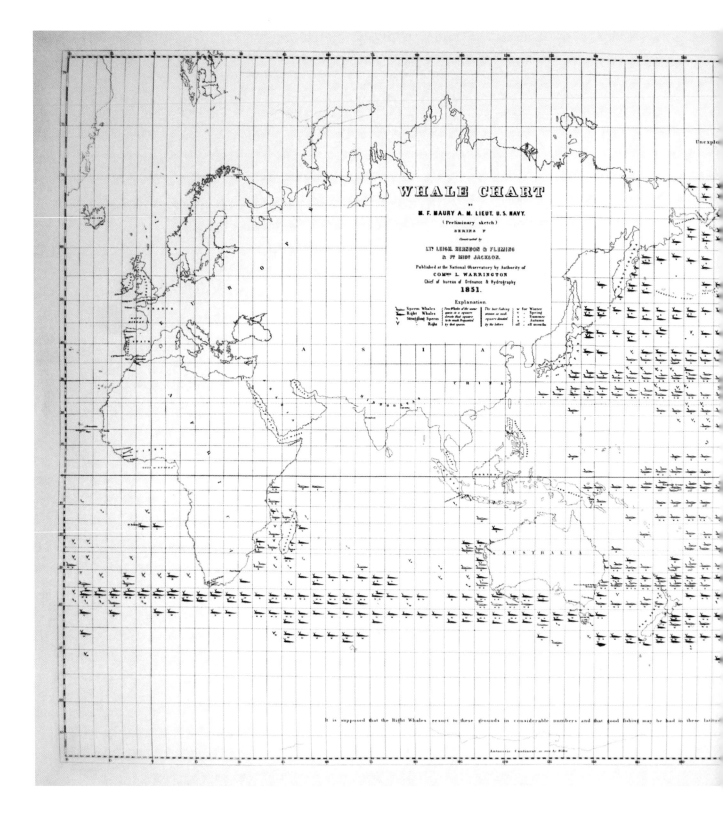

WHALE CHART

BY

M. F. MAURY A. M. LIEUT. U. S. NAVY.

(Preliminary sketch)

SERIES F

Constructed by

LTS LEIGH, HERNDON & FLEMING

& PD MIDS JACKSON.

Published at the National Observatory by Authority of

COMD L. WARRINGTON

Chief of bureau of Ordnance & Hydrography

1851.

Explanation

Sperm Whales	Few Whales of the same space in a square denote that square to be much frequented by that species	The best fishing season is such square denoted by the letters	w for Winter	
Right Whales			v · Spring	
Straggling Sperm			s · Summer	
Right			a · Autumn	
			all · all months	

It is supposed that the Right Whales resort to these grounds in considerable numbers and that good fishing may be had in these latitudes

Antarctic Continent — seen by Wilkes

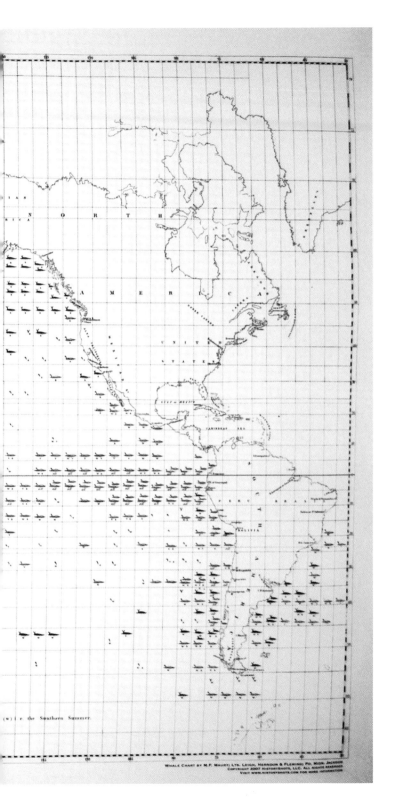

Fontaine Maury, Whaling Grounds, 1851

CHROME WHALE
Philip Hoare

Southampton, May 2011

And it is not to be imagined that nature hath refused us that meane and barred us that helpe which she hath bestowed upon many and divers other creatures: for what is that faculty we see in them when they seeme to complaine, to rejoice, to call one unto another for helpe, and bid one another to loving conjunction (as commonly they doe) by the use of their voice, but a kind of speech? And shall not they speake among themselves that speake and utter their minde unto us and we to them?

'The Apology of Raymond Sebond', *The Essays of Montaigne*

At the University of Southern Maine in Portland, Dr John Wise and his colleagues are conducting a series of extraordinary experiments. In a high-tech laboratory on their New England campus they are growing sperm whale cells, taken from whale populations around the world. Sailing westwards from the Sea of Cortez on a cruise which would take five years to complete, the crew of the research vessel *Odyssey* – a ninety-three foot, steel-hulled ketch – called at known whale locations from Kiribati and the Galápagos Islands in the Pacific, to Western Australia, Sri Lanka, the Maldives and Seychelles, Mauritius in the Indian Ocean, then to the mid-Atlantic, the Canaries, and the Mediterranean.

I wonder if they made appointments? Or perhaps they consulted a whale timetable, just as Ahab consulted his charts, whilst his real-life equivalents pored over their own cetological maps of these oceans such as Fontaine Maury's famous nineteenth-century survey of whale stocks. Published in 1851, the same year in which *Moby-Dick* appeared, and filled with whales ready to hunt, this was a document as imperially inflected as the pink-shaded dominion of the British Empire.

As an update of Maury's map, the *Odyssey*'s new cetacean survey reflects the transglobal presence of its subject, *Physeter macrocephalus*: the world's largest predator, possessor of the biggest brain, and majestic ruler of another empire entirely. Sperm whales inhabit every ocean; despite our best efforts to wipe them out, their population still stands at around 360,000 animals. If humans are endemic to the land, then whales are so to the sea; and indeed, underlying the *Odyssey*'s selective census are potentially worrying implications for our own species, as Dr Wise *et al* note in the scientific journal, *Chemosphere*: 'Because this species is an apex mammalian predator in the ocean, it reflects what might be expected for humans who depend on the ocean for food and in that sense may serve as a sentinel for human health as well.'[1]

In fact, what Dr Wise and his team have discovered as a result of the *Odyssey*'s explorations is nothing less than shocking: the notion that, because of its unique position at the top of the oceanic food chain, and because of its unique physiology, the sperm whale may be the most polluted animal in the ocean, if not the world. And as ever, it is the species that is at the top of the earthly food chain which is to blame.

Sailing from island to island in pursuit of their prey, armed with a crossbow and dart loaded with a fifty-millimetre-long steel cylinder, the collectors (rather than hunters) of the *Odyssey* took aim at their unwitting donor's rear flanks – 'a location that has been shown to elicit the fewest reactions'. From each animal they removed a plug of blubber and skin, which was frozen to minus twenty degrees centigrade within minutes of retrieval, in the same way one puts plant cuttings in plastic bags. The samples were then brought back to Maine, where, in Petri dishes smeared with a red jelly, the cultivating medium, the cells began to grow. In a way, the whole project is reminiscent of James Cook's or Charles Darwin's voyages, collecting rare samples of flora and fauna from worlds new to Western science or natural philosophy.

In the atmospherically controlled, antiseptic environs of the university laboratory, with indie rock roaring from a ghetto blaster, one of Dr Wise's young colleagues deftly adjusts the electron microscope's eyepiece so that I may peer into the world of whales-in-the-making. The tiny cells I see resemble the specks that dart in front of my eyes in the sun's glare; like urgent atoms, they are invested with the energy of their vital, gargantuan origins. The long, amoeba-like strands, stained green with fluorescent dye to make them more visible, replicate almost virally, doubling each day. It is hardly believable that each might grow into a monster – although the word is apt, since its root lies in the Latin, *monstrum*, an omen.

Yet these experiments are not being carried out for the sake of mere ingenuity – although they conjure up notions of a Frankenstein's whale, a genetically manipulated Leviathan awaiting the final spark of existence. Nor are they the product of a love of whales, for all that the offices are decorated with posters of cetaceans, and a furry toy whale lies on the couch, giving the anodyne rooms the air of a whale-mad teenager's bedroom. On the contrary: these measured, concentrated activities have a definite and awful purpose.

Dr Wise began his investigations using samples from bowhead whales, *Balaena mysticetus*, easier to come by than sperm whales, since these massive, blubber-heavy Arctic cetaceans are still hunted by the Inuit in Alaska, under the aboriginal exceptions granted by the 1986 International Whaling Commission moratorium on the hunting of great whales. Like many others, both scientists and civilians, John Wise was fascinated by the discovery of stone and ivory Inuit harpoon heads, imbedded in recently examined bowhead carcases, which appeared to indicate great longevity in the whales. When scientists analysed these specimens using levels of aspartic acid found in the eye, they concluded that these whales may live for up to three hundred years, and are thus the oldest mammals. Bowhead whales still alive now may have been swimming in the seas before Herman Melville wrote *Moby-Dick*.[2]

Whale longevity is one of the most tantalising aspects of the expanding science of cetology, not least because it raises as many questions as it supplies answers. Shortly before last February's whale symposium at Peninsula Arts in Plymouth, the results were released of a necropsy carried out on a fin whale, *Balaenoptera physalus*, that had stranded in a Danish fjord the previous summer, 2010. This animal was thought to be around fifteen to twenty years old. Yet scientific analysis showed it to be blind, arthritic, and 140 years old – thereby revising substantially the expected lifespan of this species.[3]

Such notions of extreme longevity set Dr Wise on a new train of thought. He wondered why such whales had not succumbed to the pathological conditions that circumscribe our human lives. Were they not susceptible to certain cancers, for instance, caused by pollutants in the world's oceans? These questions held an importance for the third cetacean subject of Dr Wise's research: the North Atlantic right

Right Whale, Cape Cod Bay. 2010. Philip Hoare.

whale, *Eubalaena glacialis*. This whale, a close cousin of the bowhead, is possibly as long-lived, and certainly even more threatened. Fewer than four hundred of these ponderous, shore-hugging cetaceans forage off the north-eastern coast of America, passing Maine's own coast in their search for the minute copepods, zooplankton barely bigger than a grain of rice, on which they feed.

I've often seen these whales off Provincetown at the tip of Cape Cod, where they return in late winter from their calving grounds off Florida and Georgia. On one memorable occasion the previous February, I had been cycling along Herring Cove when I caught sight of what looked like a black-sailed windsurfer in the distance, at the tip of Race Point where Cape Cod Bay meets the Atlantic. Climbing off my bike, hands gloved against the cold, I peered through my binoculars at the dark triangle held proud of the water, and realised it was the fluke of a right whale. It was a little like seeing a sea monster.

After half an hour of trudging through shifting sand and clumps of marram grass that created concentric circles around themselves in the winter winds, I crested a dune to see the shore falling away beneath me, and on its flats, a flock of black-backed gulls. As I stumbled down, the birds rose as one, like an avian stage curtain, to reveal an amazing sight. Barely fifty metres off shore, cavorting in the waves, was a group of six or seven whales. It was difficult to tell exactly how many because of what they were doing. Rolling around in the surf, throwing shapes in the air, they formed what is known as a 'surface-active group', an innocent term for such wanton behaviour. With their ebony bodies, their broad pectorals and sculpted flukes constantly appearing and disappearing, they seemed intimately engrossed in their own physicality, as if celebrating their fragile survival.

I really ought to have been watching through closed fingers, if at all, since these animals were also probably engaged in heavy petting. Right whales are highly sensitive mammals; were I to touch one with my finger – should I be so bold – the contact would send a shiver through the whale's body (and doubtless my own, too). Entirely alone, witness to an eerily quiet spectacle accompanied only by the wind and the waves, I watched the whales until the bone-numbing air got the better of me. Even as I dragged myself away from the scene, they were still tumbling around one another in the sea, all the while watched by a sole grey seal loitering on the surf's edge, as if reluctant to enter the same water wherein these giants played.

In his Portland laboratory, using samples gathered from just such a whale, sadly stranded on a New England beach, Dr Wise tested for twenty metallic elements, from lead to mercury. To do so, he used his own chemical sources in turn, cited in the same way a literary critic cites his sources, in an accidentally poetic, geo-specific shopping list –

Lead chromate (PbCrO4), demeolchicine, and potassium chloride (KCl) were purchased from Sigma/Aldrich (St. Louis, MO). Giemsa stain was purchased from Biomedical Specialities (Santa Monica, CA) … Crystal violet, methanol, and acetone were purchased from J.T. Baker (Phillipsburg, NJ) … Cosmic calf serum (CCS) was purchased from Hyclone, (Logan, UT). Tissue culture dishes, flasks, and plastic ware were purchased from Corning (Acton, MA)[4]

– one which evokes a science-fiction mall in which anything might be bought, even new life itself, and where one might meet a modern Victor Frankenstein, pushing his trolley along aisles ranged with animal extracts and obscure preparations more akin to some ancient tribal religion, all the while declaring, 'To examine the causes of life, we must first have recourse to death.'[5]

Working, not in the realms of early nineteenth-century fiction, but within the rigorous reality of contemporary epistemology, and using the other samples of sperm whale tissue retrieved by the *Odyssey*, Dr Wise and his team found high concentrations of chromium in both species of whale, far beyond any other pollutant. How could he explain this, I asked him as we sat in his office on President's Day, on an otherwise deserted campus? The February air outside was chilly; the sea even more so, as I could attest, having swum in it the day before from the little island that hangs off Portland, reached by a ferry that docks alongside a larger-than-life mural of a whale painted on the corrugated sides of a huge wharfside building. It seemed this city was haunted by whales, even as their living cells were being cultured in its laboratories.

The rest of America might be on holiday, but that Monday morning the team were hard at work as usual. John Wise smiled almost self-

Portland Maine Mural. 2010. Philip Hoare.

effacingly as he slowly, deliberately outlined his terrible hypothesis, like a doctor delivering bad news.

Male sperm whales in particular may travel more than a thousand kilometres a month, traversing entire oceans. On these watery peregrinations they pass close by to human civilisation, where they may encounter, unbeknownst to themselves, the output from chemical plants set near or on the coast. Rather than ingest the chromium through the water, Dr Wise suggested, the whales may be breathing it in through the air itself.

Sperm whales take enormous amounts of oxygen into their lungs as they ready themselves for their search for food – generally squid, which forms ninety per cent of the diet of many populations of sperm whales. Since these cephalopods are mostly found at great depths, the whales may dive more than a mile into the ocean, and can stay down there for up to two hours. In order to accomplish such a submarine feat, a sperm whale supercharges its blood with oxygen. It then collapses its lungs and folds its ribcage, which is lubricated with mucus, before tucking its paddle-shaped fins into its flanks like an aircraft's undercarriage.

It is an utter transformation. As the whale shuts down all its internal organs save its brain and its heart, its exterior actually changes shape, the bulbous head becoming narrow and hydrodynamic in readiness for a marathon descent. Given this enormous, elemental transposition, this exchange of air and water carried out so many times each day, sperm whales are, perhaps more than any other whale, susceptible to contaminants in the atmosphere.

It is an awful irony. Just as these gigantic creatures are identified from above by their angled blow at forty-five degrees to the surface – a terrible advertisement to the whalers of Melville's time – so this same marker of our shared relationship is poisoning their bodies, since we have poisoned the air. Little wonder that they seem so eager to leave our element for theirs.

Like radiation, this peril is invisible but profound. And in a further, yet more disturbing proposition, John Wise and his colleagues suggest that the effect may be most marked on the whales' fertility. As Hal

Tiaki, Kaikoura, New Zealand. 2010. Philip Hoare.

Whitehead points out, sperm whales are a *K*-selected species 'in which populations are controlled mainly by competition among their members for resources'.[6] They are enormous in both body and brain, and consequently enormously slow to breed. It is an exquisite conundrum: their brains are big to allow them to feed so efficiently, using their sonar; they are so big because their brains are big. And just as our own brains may be incapable of understanding some things, as the astronomer Martin Rees recently commented – questioning whether or not there are answers beyond the capability of human science, because we don't even know how to ask the questions – so, conversely, we may underestimate the ability of the cetacean brain, operated by an animal so large we cannot comprehend it, to ask the kind of questions we also do not know how to ask.[7]

If the years of hunting effectively destroyed the collective health of generations of whales – albeit fewer generations than lived by we humans – then this new threat, levied in the uneasy truce of the 1986 moratorium – has potentially disastrous implications for sperm whales and other cetaceans.

It is not as if the risks to whales weren't already there in abundance, from a changing climate and an acidifying ocean altering the pattern of their food sources, to the ever-growing threat of anthropogenic noise, bycatch, and ship strikes. Like the beluga whales of the Canadian St Lawrence waterway, whose bodies are so tainted that when they die, their carcases must be destroyed as toxic waste, sperm whales are especially exposed to the heavy metals and PCBs that enter their bodies through the food chain, by the simple expedient of their efficiency at feeding themselves. The idea that what is life-giving may also be fatal is reminiscent of the Pacific albatross chicks documented by the photographer Chris Jordan, dying from stomachs filled with plastic detritus fed to them by their well-meaning parents, a mirror of the medieval pelican plucking feathers from its breast to allow its infants to suckle on its blood.

Dr Wise's further conclusions are yet more disturbing, constituting, as they do, a threat to the very future of the animals. Although whale longevity suggests that they may be able to survive the immediate pathological effects of pollution, Wise hypothesises that such contamination may cause chromosomal damage analogous to Down syndrome in human beings, and may work itself out in new generations of sperm whales, and those yet to be born.

One area that Dr Wise has identified as a possible source of contamination is the Australian state of Queensland. This north-eastern corner of the country is more readily associated with the Great Barrier Reef, a place of apparent purity, an underwater paradise. Here fifteen hundred species of fish live on nine hundred coral islands, themselves composed of four hundred species of hard and soft coral; two hundred species of birds nest or roost; dugong – marine mammals once mistaken by early sailors for mermaids, and still hunted by Aboriginal people – graze in shallow, bath-water seas; and humpbacks pass by on their migration southwards down the eastern coast of Australia to spend the winter feeding on sand eels in the Southern Ocean. I've seen these same whales diving off the Tasman Peninsula, silhouetted against the highest cliffs in the Southern Hemisphere, while beetle-browed albatrosses wheel overhead. The virginal whiteness of the whales' undersides – much paler than those of their Atlantic counterparts – seems to speak of their Edenic state.

But just as those antipodean humpbacks appear to be thriving in the post-moratorium age – bringing ten per cent more calves with them each year as they return to the Australian coast after breeding in Polynesian seas – so these same waters may present them and their cousins with their greatest threat. As Dr Wise and his fellow authors note, Queensland is also home to Australia's chromium-emitting industry, which each year discharges ten tons or more of chromium into the atmosphere. And although Dr Wise and his colleagues found the highest levels of chromium in sperm whales sampled off the remote Pacific islands of Kiribati – as high as those found in humans suffering from chromium-induced lung cancer – sperm whales travel great distances; Wise *et al* assume a three thousand kilometre range for the whales they sampled in Kiribati. If they reach Queensland, then the Australian emissions may be the cause of their contamination.

Chromium derivatives are found everywhere in our world: from shiny motorbikes to double yellow lines, from school buses to chrome yellow, the artist's pigment. Yet that same colour which evokes the sun also signals for danger. The Greek *chroma* means the *quality* of colour. It is a word implicit with the light it absorbs or reflects, just as the white-

Tasmanian Whale. 2010. Philip Hoare.

ness which is all colour so appalled Ishmael, the narrator of *Moby-Dick* (literally, since to appal signifies the draining of the blood from the face, in the face of fear) as he discerned something ominous rather than innocent in such pallor. It is a further irony – one which reflects those chemicals and stains assembled by Dr Wise's laboratory – that the word 'chromosome' was coined from the coloured dyes used by scientists to discover it.

In those plastic Petri dishes, sperm whale cells become heralds of heresy. As a nuclear detonation which can destroy cities has its genesis in micrograms, and as our universe and light itself began in a microcosmic particle, so these incessantly dividing cells, microcosms of their begetters, belie the scale and supposed purity of the place from which they came, an ocean which man has contaminated. We have succeeded in reducing the sea to a microscope slide, turning numinous blue into toxic green.

*   *   *   *   *

As I write this, Japan, 'that double-bolted land' as Melville called it, is coming to terms with seismic shock and nuclear fallout.[8] Within hours of the tsunami, as we watched ships stranded in streets like beached whales, claims were appearing on the internet that the tragedy was a revenge for that nation's continuing whale hunt under the guise of scientific research. Some even fantasised that the terrible wave had been caused by the whales themselves. And in an even more outlandish web conspiracy, it was claimed that a whale had impaled itself in a high-rise building – a symbolic image which, thankfully, proved to be quite untrue.

What really happened that Friday, thousands of metres beneath the surface of the Pacific, was as invisible to us as the cloud of radiation drifting around the world from the Fukushima reactors blown open by the sea's destructive power. But others conclude, as they did in the aftermath of the 2004 tsunami, that cetaceans had acted as advance warnings of what was to come. Forty-eight hours before the Christchurch earthquake, on 22 February 2011, more than 190 pilot whales died on Stewart Island, off the southern tip of New Zealand's South Island, having been stranded there two days beforehand.[9] And barely a week later, on 4 March, fifty melon-headed whales washed up on the eastern Kashima shore of Japan, precursors of the foreshocks which were already being felt in Japan.[10]

There is, as yet, no conclusive scientific basis for such theories – not least because no one has yet been able to satisfactorily explain why cetaceans beach themselves. It is sufficiently strange behaviour to suggest all kinds of explanations, some more metaphysical than others. In Iris Murdoch's equally strange novel, *The Sea, The Sea*, in which the self-deluded actor Charles Arrowby retreats to a semi-derelict house on an unnamed English coast in search of 'monastic mysticism', swims obsessively in its waters and imagines – or perhaps actually sees – a maned and toothed sea serpent rear out of the waves, Arrowby's cousin James informs him, 'The sea is not all that clean … Did you know that dolphins sometimes commit suicide by leaping onto the land because they're so tormented by parasites?'; to which Charles replies, 'I wish you hadn't told me that. Dolphins are such good beasts. So even they have their attendant demons.'[11]

Seismic activity must have an effect, however, and it is probably true that cetaceans, like birds, use the Earth's electro-magnetic field for navigation. Indeed, the Maori who colonised the double islands of New Zealand, which they called Aotearoa, the land of the long white cloud, and may have followed migrating whales there from Polynesia, themselves were attuned to electro-magnetic paths in a timeless network of human and animal journeys that weave the oceans and islands together in an invisible web. The fact that the Japanese tsunami was followed by the threat of microscopic radioactive particles seemed to underline the history of another double island nation which suffered from the destruction of the first man-made cloud, mushrooming over the ocean like a perverse spout.

In a cynical denial of its name, the Pacific has ever since been the nuclear arena, one haunted by the hunted whales, as if they were auguries of that disaster, too. In *The Trying-Out of Moby-Dick*, published in 1949, the literary critic Howard P. Vincent saw Moby Dick as the literary incarnation of Mocha Dick, the legendary whale on which it was modelled, and which vengefully roamed the Pacific sinking ships. In Melville's modernist augury, itself uncontained by its age, the White Whale had become a mythical creature 'ubiquitous in time and place. Yesterday he sank the *Pequod*; within the past two years he has breached five times; from a New Mexico desert, over Hiroshima and Nagasaki, and most recently, at Bikini atoll.'[12] Vincent was writing at the same time as the Japanese nation, defeated by atomic war, was encouraged by the occupying Allied Powers to turn its decommissioned navy into a whaling fleet in order to feed its starving people.

Around the same time, too, the American artist Gilbert Wilson became obsessed with Melville's novel; he spent the next thirty years of his life painting it. In a 1952 essay for the *Bulletin of the Atomic Scientist*, Wilson wrote that, a century after its publication, the story had become an allegory of atomic conflict, and Captain Ahab's 'insane pursuit of Moby Dick into the Sea of Japan' analogous to America's 'atrocious nuclear experiments and explosions in the same area'. Wilson saw the whale as 'the power within the atom. Because I think we have to regard the Whale as the great Dragon ... which appears in all mythology, and which as we know symbolised *both* Good and Evil ... a tremendous embodiment of force.'[13] Two years later, when the first nuclear submarine, *Nautilus*, was launched in 1954, it was lubricated with spermaceti since it does not freeze in extreme temperatures. Its successors are even now moving silently through those same Pacific depths using sonar inspired by whales, just the *Voyager* space probe and the Hubble telescope are spinning into outer space, similarly oiled.[14]

As contemporary commentators evoked Frankenstein's creation in the disaster at Fukushima, they echoed the literary critic Mario Praz, who, in 1968, saw Mary Shelley's haunted novel, itself a critique of her husband's attempt 'to pry into the hidden laws of Nature', as an augury 'of Ahab's pursuit of Moby Dick in Frankenstein's relentless, Heaven-assigned chase of the monster'.[15] The comparison is not coincidental. Melville acquired his own copy of *Frankenstein; or, The Modern Prometheus* on his visit to London in 1849, immediately before he began to write *Moby-Dick; or, The Whale*; and the doctor's pursuit of his creature into the Arctic is undertaken on a whale-ship whose captain is attempting to locate the legendary North-West Passage.[16] Meanwhile, the poem that inspired both Melville and Shelley, Samuel Taylor Coleridge's *Rime of the Ancient Mariner*, with its own tale of burden, obsession and evil, could also be seen as an allegory of nuclear power, as much as it is reflected in the fated albatross parents feeding plastic to their young from the Pacific gyre.

That ever-circling ocean, of *Moby-Dick*, of the explorations of Cook, of the first missionaries of the eighteenth century and of the expanding American empire of the nineteenth, remains even now, in the twenty-first century, the great unknown. In the age of Yankee whaling it was coursed by whale-ships, the oil tankers of their day, busily rendering down its cetaceans, as Maury's map shows. Today this same sea is the backyard to both the world's most developed and developing nations. In his book, *Atlantic: a vast ocean of a million stories*, Simon Winchester points out that the modern world began around the Mediterranean, which ceded power to the Atlantic with America's uprise. The future has moved to the east, to an ocean barely two centuries old in the eyes of Western history.

That yawning, freighted space seems so blank and so full of potential at the same time. From the bland two-dimensions of the atlas, its blue expanse appears entirely empty, antediluvian evidence of the continental weighting of the West. Yet it is filled with life, with twenty-five thousand islands and, as Hal Whitehead explains, numberless 'ultra-social' pods of sperm whales that roam and associate in nations of their own, bound by discrete dialects of clicks. What kind of disasters did they suffer during that terrible seismic shift? What will they yet suffer, should the sea itself become radioactive?[17] Like the thousands of animals that died in the oil spill in the Gulf of Mexico, their fate is unknown to us, vastly outweighed, in our eyes, by the human suffering in Japan. Yet these things are not unconnected, especially if you believe that cetaceans, like the great apes and elephants, possess such sentience and the capability for emotion that they ought to be classified as 'non-human persons', as the 2010 conference on cetacean rights at the University of Helsinki declared.[18] As Nietzsche wrote in *Beyond Good and Evil*, a philosophical update on Victor Frankenstein's self-inflicted dilemma,

He who fights with monsters should be careful lest he thereby become a monster. And if thou gaze long into an abyss, the abyss will also gaze into thee.[19]

*   *   *   *   *

We see all too often in two dimensions. As I watch the sea rise before me to the far shore, it seems to be a panorama, an animated strip, a drama played out for my benefit. What then does the sperm whale see, since it lacks stereoscopic sight? Does it have to piece the world together, using its gigantic brain, as I do, too? The ocean is unknowable, and so we continue to ignore it. It is the way we have to live. Too much beauty would kill us. So we kill it in turn.

On Nantucket, off Cape Cod's southern elbow, where the wealth of the island is attested by multi-million dollar mansions and their decorative widows' walks, the memory of the years of whaling is delicately but vigorously preserved in its beautifully appointed museum. Its relics all deserve and have had my attention, but on my return to this place, I am struck by two particular exhibits. The first is the eighteen-foot jaw of a sperm whale, so miraculous that when it was displayed in an earlier incarnation of the museum – in essence, a kind of cabinet of curiosities – the great showman P. T. Barnum sought to buy it for his rather more commercial purposes on Broadway where, he claimed, its exhibition would benefit mankind. Its owners declined, and the bone now stands upright in the museum's lower gallery, witness to an impossibility: a bull sperm whale measuring eighty-seven feet, twenty feet longer than the largest known contemporary representative of the species and proof, as if it were needed, that so many of our assumptions about these creatures are wrong.[20]

The other magnificent display in Nantucket is set upstairs in a dark but lustrously glittering glass cabinet, surrounded by portraits of whaling captains. Here stand row upon row of whale teeth, pulled out of just such a jawbone and etched with scrimshaw designs by bored sailors. Close by lie other bones carved into pastry cutters or articulated yard winders known as swifts. These cream-coloured artefacts are examples of a now celebrated folk art, whalish tributes to New England's new order. As I walk around these floor-to-ceiling vitrines, I am seized by a strange fantasy: that in a future age we may be forced to repatriate these trophies to their rightful owners, just as aboriginal remains collected by other colonisers have since been returned to their tribes. Perhaps the whales will then carry them to some abyssal trench, to inter them reverently as memorials to generations lost to human commerce.

How ill rewarded is the whale! A recent report from Flinders University, Adelaide, notes that the population of twelve thousand sperm whales in the Southern Ocean are now carbon negative in their contribution to the warming world. Expelling fifty tonnes of iron-rich faeces each year, they fertilise the growth of phytoplankton. As a result, their bodily functions – once thought to contribute to climate change by discharging carbon dioxide through exhaled breath – in fact remove four hundred thousand tonnes of carbon from the atmosphere via the increased plant growth they encourage. In a further indictment of our actions, the researchers calculated if the age of hunting had not happened – the rush for oil which decimated the whales, the rush for oil which changed our climate – the population of sperm whales would have drawn more than two million tonnes of carbon from our overheated atmosphere.[21]

We all use the whale. I use it to write books. Artists use it to make art. Scientists use it to make science. What difference is there in our exploitation? Now we assign a new role for the whale, as a depth-gauge of the environment we have bespoiled. Presumably unconscious of its latest designation, down there in the depths, does it swim in virgin waters to the cemetery of its ancestors, mournfully revisiting their bones as do African elephants? Or has this last resort too become a sump for our debris, where plastic breaks down to insidiously enter the food chain, and where radioactivity settles out of sight, sitting out its half-life, a toxic time bomb ticking away?

We feel responsible for whales because, however huge or wild they may be, we have ultimate power over them. That is the essential paradox. We have the final decision over their fate: the dominion we hold over nature is the basis of the nature of all our relationships to animals. In his *Bedside Book of Beasts*, Graeme Gibson describes how humans became disconnected from nature when they first began to hunt remotely, with bow and arrow. Before that point – that fulcrum between human history and natural history – the hunters had taken the slowest member of a herd, the ailing or the weak. This process actually strengthened the greater herd; it was, in the argot of our age, sustainable.

But with the development of the projectile, the biggest, strongest individual in the herd became the target of hunters 'routinely selecting out the most genetically valuable members'.[22] Its death meant an essential component of the group was removed, and thus the group itself was affected, for the worse. The balance was thrown out of kilter. In the nineteenth and twentieth centuries, a similar step-change in technology enabled the whalers to hunt the fastest, biggest whales – the gigantic fin and blue whales. At first, the pressure was taken off the sperm whale population by this increased efficiency, but soon they came under renewed attack, all the more effective since these cetaceans are so highly social and therefore easier to cull in great number. In 1910, just forty-three sperm whales were officially taken. In 1964, the toll was twenty-nine thousand. (Totals of hunted whales were drastically under-reported in the post-war peak, a discrepancy of one hundred thousand animals in the southern hemisphere alone. The reason was political: under Communist five-year plans, productivity could not stay still; each year had to be exponentially better than the last. Thus the conserving strictures of the IWC met the dictatorial demands of the CCCP. In the Cold War, as ever, whales were the losers.)[23]

The lack of big males to mate with females may have affected the size of individuals, as the evidence of the past seems to testify. The witness of that extraordinary jawbone in Nantucket's whaling museum is joined by another, from under the giant gothic iron and glass conservatory that is the Natural History Museum in Oxford. Here the visitor has no sooner walked in the door than she or he is confronted with an even larger sperm whale mandible, dangling by a crude rusty hinge which pierces it like a ring through a bull's nose. This belonged, so its label says, to an even larger animal, eighty-eight feet in length. It is as if we created dinosaurs out of our own recent history; the monsters we slew, now no more. Equally, the fact that these animals are so long-lived – sperm whales are thought to reach at least one hundred years of age – exacerbates the issue of how long it may take whales to recover from those years of hunting, since it takes so long for such massive specimens to reach maturity. The very basis of our notional knowledge of these creatures is challenged by their longevity. How can we study animals that outlive us? Perhaps it should be the other way around.

After ten years watching them around the world, what whales are, and what they mean, what they might be, and what they might mean, still obsesses me. We are in the middle of their story, rather than at its end. Their sense of elemental otherness, suspended beyond our dimensional parameters, seems to sharpen the distance between our species and all others; a notional dominion. We account ourselves superior for our ability to travel in time and space, yet these are fearful prospects: the fear of being foundered in the past, the fear of being afraid of the future, the fear of staying still. Forever restless, we must escape the terrors and continue the chase, as if prey and hunter combined. Yet we are always and forever lost in the madness of our own making.

And all the while the whale abides, a symbol of titanic struggle and evolutionary change, an echo of our past and future, yet utterly unchanged compared to our puny span. Little wonder it fascinates artists and scientists, since it represents everything that lies just beyond our grasp. If we are redeemed at all, it is by our ability to bear witness to beauty as well as to horror. I understand less about whales now than I did when I started my journey; the questions merely multiply, like those cetacean cells in Dr Wise's dishes. I ought not be surprised. After all, even Ishmael had to admit of his grand and mysterious muse, whose measure he so magnificently failed to encompass: 'I know him not, and never will.'[24]

www.leviathan-or-the-whale.blogspot.com

Source Notes

1   John Pierce Wise Sr, Roger Payne, Sandra S. Wise, Carolyne LaCerte, James Wise, Christy Gianios Jr, W. Douglas Thompson, Christopher Perkins, Tongzhang Zheng, Cairong Zhu, Lucille Benedicy and Iain Kerr, 'A global assessment of chromium pollution using sperm whales (*Physeter macrocephalus*) as an indicator species', *Chemosphere*, 75 (2009), p.1462. The lowest levels of chromium observed were in whales near the Canary Islands, and those off the coast of Sri Lanka.

2   http://www.gi.alaska.edu/ScienceForum/ASF15/1529.html, accessed 18 March 2011.

3   http://marinelife.about.com/b/2010/11/04/denmark-fin-whale-was-140-years-old.htm; http://www.greenfudge.org/2010/11/09/fin-whale-that-stranded-on-danish-shores-was-140-years-old/, accessed 15 March 2011.

4   Tania Li Chen, Sandra S. Wise, Scott Kraus, Fariba Shaffiey, Kaitlynn M. Levine, W. Douglas Thompson, Tracy Romano, Todd O'Hara and John Pierce Wise Sr, 'Particulate hexavalent chromium is cytotoxic and genotoxic to the North Atlantic right whale (*Eubalaena glacialis*) lung and skin fibroblasts', *Environmental and Molecular Mutagenesis*, 50 (2009), p. 388.

5   Mary Shelley, *Frankenstein; Or, The Modern Prometheus*, from *Three Gothic Novels: Walpole, The Castle of Otranto / Beckford, Vathek / Mary Shelley, Frankenstein* (Harmondsworth: Penguin, 1968/1975), p. 311.

6   Hal Whitehead, *Sperm Whales: Social Evolution in the Ocean* (Chicago, MA: University of Chicago Press, 2003), p. 13.

7 In conversation with Melvyn Bragg, *King James Bible: The Book That Changed The World*, broadcast BBC 2, 12 March 2011.

8 Herman Melville, 'The Advocate', *Moby-Dick* (Los Angeles and London: Arion Press/University of California Press, 1979), p. 114. Japan was still a closed state when *Moby-Dick* was written. 'If that double-bolted land, Japan, is ever to become hospitable, it is the whale-ship alone to whom the credit will be due; for already she is on the threshold.' *Ibid*.

9 '197 beached pilot whales die', *The Independent*, 22 February 2011. As I update this text, a pod of sixty pilot whales threaten to strand on South Uist off the western coast of Scotland.

10 'Rescuers save 22 melon-headed whales' UPI report, 6 March 2011, upi.com, accessed 4 May 2011.

11 Iris Murdoch, *The Sea, The Sea*, (London: Chatto & Windus, 1978), p. 460, p. 443.

12 Howard P. Vincent, *The Trying-Out of Moby-Dick*, (Illinois: Southern Illinois University Press, 1949), p. 176–7. For a visualisation of the nuclear map, see: http://www.youtube.com/watch?v=LLCF7vPanrY&feature=player_embedded#at=347

13 Elizabeth A. Schultz, *Unpainted to the Last: Moby-Dick and Twentieth-Century American Art* (Lawrence, KS: University Press of Kansas, 1995), p. 178.

14 The US Navy had launched its first submarine, the *Intelligent Whale*, in 1872. It flooded and was condemned the same day, after eight years of tests and the deaths of thirty-nine men. In 1919, the *Illustrated London News* published images from 'The War in the Air Exhibition of coloured photographs' in New Bond Street, 'illustrating the wonderful work of the Royal Air Force during the war'. They included two aerial photographs of blue whales, indicating 'how easy it was for observers in the air to mistake a whale for a submarine. In half-lights, these huge monsters bore a strong resemblance to a submerged U-boat, and, as the rule in war was "When in doubt, bomb", a good many of them were killed by our aircraft.'(5 April 1919)

15 Mario Praz, Introductory Essay in *Three Gothic Novels*, pp. 31–2, p. 26.

16 The opening and closing scenes in *Frankenstein* (1818) evoke the work of the Arctic whaler and explorer, William Scoresby. His *An Account of the Arctic Regions* (1821), was another of the books from which Melville stole in *Moby-Dick* – see Philip Hoare, *Leviathan or, The Whale* (London: Fourth Estate, 2008), pp. 287–97. Scoresby left on his first Arctic voyage in 1814, at which point Mary Shelley had been living in Dundee for nearly three years, witness to the port's own whaling and expeditionary ships.

17 In *Atlantic*, Winchester also notes that, up until the late 1970s, British-chartered ships dumped more than twenty-nine thousand tons of 'highly active radioactive waste', by products of nuclear power and the weapons industry, encased in cement-lined steel barrels, into the Atlantic, four hundred miles west of Land's End, as well as another sixteen thousand tons in the English Channel, with tertiary sites in the Irish Sea and off Scotland. The people of Cornwall and Devon were duly reassured that any material washed ashore would be subject to 'dispersion and dilution': Simon Winchester, *Atlantic* (London: Harper Press, 2010), p. 356. For more on radioactive contamination, whales, Japan, Iceland and Britain, see: http://blog.seattlepi.com/candacewhiting/2011/05/04/japan-is-not-alone-the-whaling-nations-of-europe-and-iceland-are-also-exposed-to-radioactive-contamination/. It was recently reported that minke whales, hunted by Japan's coastal whaling operation (itself endangered by the tsunami) have been found to be contaminated with traces of radioactive material.['Atomic whales', James Fair, *BBC Wildlife*, September 2011]

18 http://cetaceanconservation.com.au/cetaceanrights/

19 Quoted, Vincent, *The Trying-Out of Moby-Dick*, p. 335n.

20 In *The Natural History of the Sperm Whale*, the seminal book on this seminal ceta-
    cean, and a rich source for Melville, Thomas Beale records a male whale caught
    in 'the Japan fishery' which he personally measured as being eighty-four feet in
    length. Thomas Beale, *The Natural History of the Sperm Whale* (London: John Van
    Voorst, 1839), p. 15.

21 http://inform.com/special-interests/whale-poop-fights-climate-change-study-
    964820a#, accessed 16 March 2011. Baleen whales may contribute even more
    to this effect: see: http://www.newscientist.com/article/dn18807-whale-poop-is-
    vital-to-oceans-carbon-cycle.html, accessed 14 July 2011.

22 Graeme Gibson, *The Bedside Book of Beasts* (London: Bloomsbury, 2010), pp. 3–4.

23 Figures from Maurizio Wurtz and Nadia Repetto, *Dolphins and Whales* (Italy:
    White Star, 2003). See also Whitehead, *Sperm Whales: Social Evolution in the Ocean*,
    pp. 19–20, and Sarah Lazarus, *Troubled Waters: The Changing Fortunes of Whales and
    Dolphins* (London: Natural History Museum, 2006), p. 78.

24 Melville, 'The Tail', *Moby-Dick*, p. 388.

Moby-Dick book collection. 2011. Peninsula Arts Plymouth.

THERE'S MORE TO WHALING THAN WHALES
Anthony Caleshu

"These turtles are a delicious food … with these, ships usually supply
themselves for a great length of time, and make a great saving of other
provisions." Owen Chase, *Narrative of the Most Extraordinary and Distressing*
Shipwreck of the Whale-Ship Essex, 1821.

We'd been wooing whales like women once wooed us
when we sprang a leak off the guano rich coast of Ecuador.

Galápagos Giants – so gentle under foot – were soon
strewn aboard, wandering freely over deck

or stowed away in the hold. For her gaze heavenward
we planned to love one, but the others

we'd sparingly steep in the stock of our sweet and sour soup.
It wasn't until a month after – anchored and shirt-free –

that we spotted a shoal off the lee bow.
Remember the sea as fragile as a boiled egg?

the sky as unforgiving as a spoon…
Now recall how effortlessly our pet used to sink and swim;

how she used to rise so buoyantly to whatever challenge
she set herself…
But this was before the stoving,

before the celerity, before we were reminded
that a whale's head is as hard as a horse's hoof,

which, it turns out, is even harder than a turtle's shell.

'Dead Men Don't Bite'. 2008.
Plaster, sheep, pig bones.

Chapters. 2010.
Dress embroidered with
135 chapters from
Moby-Dick.

DOMINION
Angela Cockayne

Bath, 2011

The exhibition *Dominion* has been central to the first British Whale Festival, a project which seeks to explore the links between science and art, literature, and the associations explored in the wonderfully mythic masterpiece that is Herman Melville's *Moby-Dick*.

For several years now, the whale has been an abiding vessel to which I have anchored my work. In particular, the white whale: the ambiguous, mysterious Moby Dick, an association that has helped me to unite my fascination with natural sciences, visual culture and contemporary art practice. The *Dominion* project took hold in the year I finally managed to complete reading *Moby-Dick* – after several failed attempts. At the time my research was investigating cultural fear and global anxiety in context of a world intent on raging war, self-destruction through denial of global warming and species extinction. In 2005, my Christmas tree was covered in white origami sperm whales.

Moby-Dick as a work hovers somewhere between natural history, philosophy, autobiography and fiction. The legendary nature of the Leviathan has attracted artists, scientists, writers, musicians and storytellers throughout the world and throughout history – from the ancient civilisations to aboriginal peoples, from nineteenth-century literature to twenty-first-century cinema. If the Greeks knew nothing of dinosaurs, they certainly knew Leviathan. Above all things, Moby Dick the whale is a shape-shifter, digressive and allusive. 'I know him not and never will', as Ishmael says. Such curiosity enables artists and writers to project an ever-changing sense of our relationship with the world onto a creature that in reality identifies ourselves.

Melville is not only the narrator, Ishmael, with his conflicted voice; he is Ahab, too, both 'savage' and Christian. There is no dominion in blood, bone or ash. Perhaps that is why I am drawn to the ambiguous space that the book provides. We only ever catch glimpses of the whale and ourselves reflected in his whiteness. Likewise, the book is packed with non-verbal text and unutterable otherness. This is at the core of the exhibition of *Dominion* and the essence of what I have tried to preserve in my research, a visceral response exploring both scientific evidence alongside a mythical interpretation of the Leviathan.

A compendium of cetology, anthropology, obsession, prophesy, self-destruction and morality, *Moby-Dick* is saturated with metaphor. Despite its beautiful and often convoluted language it is as potent today as when it was first published 160 years ago. It is a novel ahead of its time, one which allows the reader to bring their own meaning to the text. Ultimately 'meaning' resides somewhere between the text, the author and the reader – a negotiated space. I have read the book twice now, six years apart. My second 'reading' felt like a different book: I came to it with my own shifted self and new associations. It is in this context that *Dominion* seeks to investigate with an unspoken 'truth' a primordial response, using teeth, bone, and hair to illuminate a text, one which seems to operate at a subliminal level.

In relation to my own practice and the project, *Dominion* embraces interdisciplinary practice not only in the methodology used in relation to specific mediums, casting, film, photography, textiles and sculpture, but also a methodology in relation to different disciplines traversing the domains of science, art, music and literature. It draws upon research that is fielded from different disciplines and research communities. In a world where meaning operates in a 'negotiated space' hopefully the 'un-packing' of a work or the 'content' is available for a wider audience to see beyond the usual confines of a fine art audience.

Through working with scientists my white coat syndrome has vanished. I have come to realise how similar and vulnerable both artist and scientist are in presenting their work. Like art, science is experimental, and although based on empirical evidence and data rather than a reliance of intuition, it is correspondingly presenting 'hypotheses' for analysis, in the same way an artist uses pertinent materials and imagery. 'All knowledge is cloaked', as the seventeenth-century philosopher Thomas Browne wrote.

The work made for the project has been research led, finding the most simple and effective materials to communicate my response to this with the lightest of touch, in the alchemy of drawing together materials, simply and intuitively. I don't seek to illustrate my findings, but navigate my position in relation to my subject and the context it operates in. Hitching a ride on the back of a mythical whale has enabled me to re-contextualise my practice whilst simultaneously providing a thematic and beguiling muse. Unexpectedly, I began to enjoy the research question and activity as much as the making. The new concern of how to reconcile the two became paramount.

My investigation for the project over the past six years has been uncharted and absorbing, embracing scientific 'evidence' alongside anthropology, prose and mythology. The project has taken me on an imaginative voyage from Nantucket to the South Pacific and back again from the comfort of a sofa, a warm laptop and an ever-growing pile of books, which conspired to obscure my own presence.

The liminal creatures I started making, using horn, teeth and coral found on strandlines, hover in the ambiguous space the whale also seems to occupy, a mammal traversing somewhere between the domains of land and ocean. Works such as *Surf and Turf*, cast-wax squid bodies with 'heads' made from coral and bone, are suggestive of a primordial past, from an eyeless pre-Cambrian era. The whale also

Cabinets. 2011. Peninsula Arts Plymouth.

'Dead Men Don't Bite'. 2011. Eco-resin boat. Peninsula Arts Plymouth.

has an ambiguous past demonstrated by its vestigial limbs, ancestral evidence of a life on land; its nearest relative is the hippopotamus.

Beyond the research, it is the making of the work that interests me; I am a prolific maker, often making several things, from which I then reselect, sometimes keeping only one or two pieces. My use of found and organic materials is integral to this project, and has helped me navigate my course. As a maker of things, the idea has often superseded the image, and the image the object. It was my intention to play or intervene with the objects I made, and I have often pushed their fragility to the limit. The wax repairs, the tidelines upon damask in the work *Nantucket Sleigh Ride*, the surfboard dings, are like scars, evidence of the work's existence beyond some obscure imagining.

The works are mostly presented in their 'raw' state, unmediated through discipline or technique. They are more about the moment of conception, the alchemy of concept and material and the visual manifestation of an idea. They are often ephemeral, existing briefly, held together often tenuously. The work is not so much about object-hood nor deliberately anti-object, in that it lacks translation. What interests me more is the act of making, the research and manifestation between the materials used and the dialogue between the works. Much of the work I make no longer exists, or perhaps only in a photograph. I will often make several similar things to end up with one; other works get recycled and superseded by new configurations if the dialogue between things becomes unfocussed.

Using detritus and found things to configure a metaphysical investigation in a physical world already over-saturated with stuff helps me to make sense of contemporary culture. The maquette seems to suffice and is less self-conscious and closer to what I'm trying to visualise. I have recently begun to use biodegradable materials for larger works, and I'm grateful to funding partners Bath Spa University and Sustainable Futures who have funded my investigation into new sustainable resins that can be composted when they've outlived their use. The orchestration of the material and provenance is very important to me. Most are found on shorelines, a place that lends itself to the liminality I seek to achieve in the works. The use of text, photography and film has also been central to *Dominion*, exploring both a sense of scale, transience, and mood worthy of this great Leviathan.

Octo-Purse. 2009. Pewter coins.

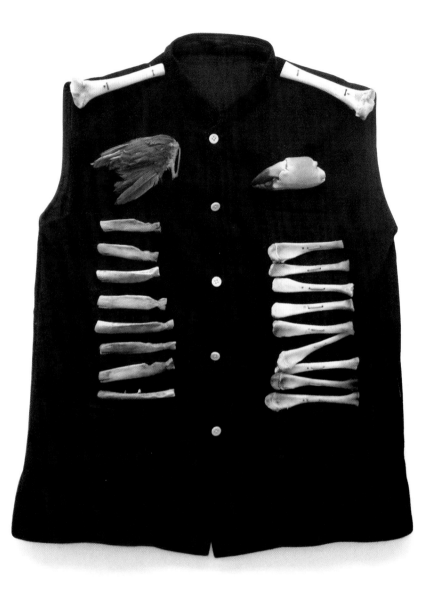

Ahab's Jacket, 2007. Bird wing, carved spare ribs, ham bones.

I approach the highly gendered text of *Moby-Dick* as an artist and as a female. The two are obviously intrinsically bound. The work *Ahab's Brides*, 2005, a set of cast-plaster sperm whale teeth arranged across the floor, investigates a fight or flight, tend or befriend response to a conflicted world, which seemed to be gnashing its teeth. Initially, I carved the heads of twentieth-century dictators like scrimshaw into the teeth. Finding this too literal, I filled these cavities and covered them in bridal lace. While the whale men of Nantucket where harvesting whales, illuminating the Industrial Revolution, the women in their hours of domestic leisure, waiting for their men to return, spent their time lace making. Ironically the Quaker wives of Nantucket suppressed their desires for self-ornamentation, preferring bedspreads; but echoed the scrimshanding of their whale men, and the exotic tattooing of Marquesan visitors to their shores in search of employment in a thriving whaling industry.

It is interesting to note that the whale as the first global commodity had many uses. I was intrigued to discover how the puritan 'Quakers with a vengeance' of such whaling communities carved utilitarian scrimshaw fancies for their wives back home. Nathaniel Philbrick describes in his book *The Heart of the Sea* how the independent wives left ashore for up to five years at a time were kept pacified with 'he's at home', whale teeth carved into the shape of a penis. The captains of some whale-ships took their wives and children to sea with them on long and cramped voyages. These 'petticoat whalers', as they were known, lived under the most horrific conditions, their presence aboard ship saved many a captain from the temptations of rum and the hospitality of South Sea maidens. Syphilis was epidemic in whaling ports; a difficult disease to explain, even back then, upon return to loved ones waiting at home.

Made from discarded children's duvets, the work *Slumber*, 2006, vertically suspended white sleeping sperm whales, represents the data from a questionnaire of what men worry about. The scale of the worry determines the scale of the whale. The data was misleading. When one hundred women were asked the same questions, they worried about everything. So the scale of the shark fins, which represented their fears, was evenly spread. Men didn't appear to worry about much; global warming, when correlated into percentages, seemed to represent their major anxiety.

Once individual works were made for *Dominion*, orchestration, curation, and the dialogue between the pieces became paramount. This is why they became mediated through the film. It was always my intention to intervene with the objects, but it was interesting to discover how the space between the objects themselves created an unexpected dialogue. The same material, edited differently, created a very different feel to the work.

The placing of an object in a space presents a new opportunity for potential dialogue. The white cube seemed to represent the white whale, and a temptation to present the whale's vaporous 'blow' and a lactating wall was superseded by the obsessive character of the book. The whale and submarine hybrid in the work *Specksynder* and the *Hubwhale*, made using lace, cuttlefish and eco resin, allowed me to represent the spatial divide and depths to which the whale has enabled our own voyages from ocean floor to outer space. Sperm whale oil is used by NASA on both submarines and satellites as it does not freeze in extreme temperatures.

A primary concern in making an object, or installation, is the fusion of concept and material or site. This involves translating concept and transforming material or site into something new. One may need to identify if one is concerned with form, materials, concept or context. This raises the question is the work conceptually led, materially driven or usually both? Work comes from making work, frequently beyond any planned intention or enquiry. I personally have to allow myself time to play and work with a lack of self consciousness in order to come up with new configurations, to avoid illustrating both the theory and the research in order to keep the work fresh and alive. Hopefully by osmosis one's work examines or assumes a critical understanding and self-awareness without mimicking the current debate or other leading contemporary artists.

Working in collaboration on *Dominion* has been a life-changing experience. I discovered Philip Hoare's film *The Hunt for Moby-Dick* quite by chance. I was overwhelmed, when I watched the film, by the striking correspondences both Philip and I had made with the white whale as an emblem of global anxiety. Together we filmed *Dominion*. We had no script, only a selection of images, artworks and Philip's film of a sperm whale underwater, which I knew in advance I wanted to project indoors. In a day we captured all the footage, responding to the artworks and location almost intuitively. Through collaboration, I have developed a greater understanding of the thread of narratives between individual works to encompass potential new readings. Equally, I have explored new relationships between individual works and to the relationship between text and image, sound and image, myth and science.

Beyond the imagery, the whale as muse reached a new height for me when I began to introduce sound to *Dominion*. Hal Whitehead's extraordinary recordings of sperm whale conversations contributed to the project, along with an eighteenth-century hymn and a haunting soundtrack composed by Nick Atkinson in response to the images. The result exceeded all my expectations. It was like breathing air into the objects themselves and distilling my intentions.

Dominion is a requiem, for what I bear witness to in my lifetime; we killed more whales in the 1960s with explosive harpoons and factory whale ships than in a hundred years of Yankee whaling. This is an apology for our exploitation of our host planet and the fellow creatures we share it with. The sperm whale is an emblematic, magnificent creature, one of many we have almost driven to extinction. It is the largest carnivore, the loudest animal, and the deepest diving. It is also the most traversed, oiling our own Cenozoic voyage through the darkest voids of ocean depths into outer space on the Hubble telescope. And it possesses the biggest brain. In the past forty years, as our own understanding of these highly intelligent creatures and their complex social behaviour has expanded, there has been a paradigm shift from exploitation to celebration; resource to wonderment. In the process the whale has become a barometer for our own ecological destiny, In *Moby-Dick* we see a gentle giant, a passive but potential predator provoked to expose our own flaws.

We killed their 'useless' calves as bait to attract their oil-rich mothers to the slaughter. 'Fiction' becomes fact and a whale with vengeance retaliates by sinking a ship. Although Owen Chase related that the whale ship *Essex* was stove by a bull whale, I believe there is a chance that the whale may have been female, protecting its calf. Hal Whitehead himself describes how passive and shy the sperm whale is. The females form strong social groups, suckle one another's calves and babysit them while their mothers feed. They act collectively to protect their offspring under attack.

My research led me to the notion of post-colonial 'collective guilt', not only over our exploitation of the whale, and the critical rejection of the ambitions of Melville as an author (who was sent into literary exile on publication of the text), but also of colonial intrusion.

While the good Quaker folk of Nantucket fought for the abolition of slavery, we continued to pursue our noble domestication of the savage. On the eighteenth-century whaling voyages, missionaries were sent out to tame the South Seas and 'savages' in order to plunder and impose their own versions of Christian democracy. How confusing this must have been to the 'natives', forbidden by the missionaries from the eating of human flesh whilst being asked to consume the body and blood of Christ in a religious act and the in name of a new 'god'. Marina Warner suggested in her Reith lecture in 1994, *Cannibal Tales*, that 'cannibalism helped to justify the presence of the invader, the settler or the trader bringing civilisation' and 'the self needs the other to establish a sense of integral identity'. In chapter fifty-seven of *Moby-Dick*, Melville declares his allegiance to the nobility of savagery and discusses this throughout the book, in his affection and admiration of his harpooner bedfellow Queequeg. Their 'platonic' relationship interweaves and binds the text. It suggests an inner conflict of 'forbidden' carnal desire.

The works *Weapons of Mass Extinction*, harpoons fashioned with bird beaks, wings and crustacean parts, and *Museum of Extinction*, two barrels drilled by cast narwhal tusks with wax hearts, explore our futile dominion and exploitation of natural resources. All the gold I owned was melted down to make a 'doubloon' and attached to the self-defeating structure. We are intrinsic to the world we plunder and destruct, but we are not the masters of creation or separate from nature. Scientists believe that the sixth mass extinction has already begun through overharvesting, habitat destruction, pollution, global warming, alien displacement and human overpopulation. After 4 billion years of evolution, human activities and influences are accelerating the rate of species extinction at an alarming rate.

Dominion exhibition, 2011.
Peninsula Arts Plymouth.

We have known for over one hundred years that carbon dioxide and man made emissions are harmful to our environment yet we have failed to act on this, even the media prefer to fuel the controversy about its 'potential' ever increasing devastating impact, rather than confront the scientific evidence. The oceans like the Amazon rain forests, filter two thirds of the oxygen we breathe. Acidification though sea temperatures rising, is harming vital microscopic plankton.

Unfortunately it appears that we must wait for a catastrophe greater than the famines in Africa, melting ice caps, even more dramatic than the post apocalyptic movies, before we face up to the problems our impact and proliferation has caused for all life form on the planet. We are I believe at a pivotal point in history, nature will address the balance but perhaps to a world without mankind if we do not face up to our responsibilities on an collective and international scale. The map is man made we must act beyond territories and plan a future that accommodates for biodiversity, sustainability and an environment for all life to flourish.

In the scheme of things, the blink of 100 years, we seem to have plundered the planet, and continue on a course to potentially devastate our own habitat, a paradise that took billions of years to evolve. Our own future like that of many species including the whale, may hang in the balance if we continue to consume unsustainably in a finite system. Save the Whale was the first international campaign that highlighted our impact on a species in the 1970s. Melville, ahead of his time, prophesised man's fallibility and capability of self-destruction in pursuit of a creature that was bigger than himself.

It's interesting to reflect that if all insects were to disappear from the earth, within fifty years all forms of life on earth would perish. We depend on them that thoroughly. But if all human beings were to disappear from the earth within fifty years all other forms of life would flourish.
— Jonas Salk

Even as I was working on the last stages of *Dominion*, fiction became fact again with the discovery of George Pollard's last ship, the *Two Brothers*, as an undersea wreck near Hawaii. George Pollard was the surviving captain of the infamous *Essex*, whose fate inspired *Moby-Dick*, as well as the cannibal craft, *Dead Men Don't Bite* in the exhibition.

'No Suicides Here'. 2011.
Salt, hair, steel. Ishmaels Raft,
2010. Eco-resin.

Thus this story of 'civilised' cannibalism, a tale of ninety-three days of survival at sea, returns to haunt us. In my final piece, the film *Rachel's Orphan* – its title taken from the last line of *Moby-Dick* – the white hunter removes the whale's lace teeth from a jaw stock, only to replace them. Meanwhile, a young Ishmael surfs on his coffin lid, having survived to tell the tale.

Bibliography

— Cousteau, Jacques and Yves Paccalet, *Jacques Cousteau--whales* (New York: H. N. Abrams, 1988). Print.

— Beale, Thomas, *The Natural History of the Sperm Whale … to Which Is Added a Sketch of a South-Sea Whaling Voyage* (London: J. Van Voorst, 1839). Print.

— Brakes, Philippa and Mark Simmonds, *Whales and Dolphins* (London: WDCS Earthscan, 2011). Print

— Bullen, Frank T., *The Cruise of the Cachelot: Around the World after Sperm Whales* (London: John Murray, 1917). Print.

— Druett, Joan and Ron Druett, *Petticoat Whalers: Whaling Wives at Sea*, 1820–1920 (Auckland: Collins, 1991). Print.

— Ellis, Richard, *Men and Whales* (New York: Knopf, 1991). Print.

— Ellis, Richard, *The Great Sperm Whale: A Natural History of the Ocean's Most Magnificent and Mysterious Creature* (Lawrence, KS: University of Kansas, 2011). Print.

— Gordon, Jonathan, *Sperm Whales* (Stillwater, MN: Voyageur, 1998). Print.

— Heffernan, Thomas Farel, *Stove by a Whale: Owen Chase and the Essex* (Middletown, CT: Wesleyan University Press, 1981). Print.

— Hoare, Philip, *Leviathan or, The Whale* (London: Fourth Estate, 2009). Print.

— Melville, Herman, *Moby Dick, or The Whale, by Herman Melville … Illustrated by Rockwell Kent* (Chicago: Lakeside, 1930). Print.

— Morris, Desmond, *The Human Animal: a Personal View of the Human Species* (New York: Crown, 1994). Print.

— Naslund, Sena Jeter and Herman Melville, *Ahab's Wife, or, the Star-gazer: a Novel* (New York: William Morrow, 1999). Print.

— Philbrick, Nathaniel, *In the Heart of the Sea: the Tragedy of the Whaleship Essex* (New York: Viking, 2000). Print.

— Roman, Joe, *Whale* (London: Reaktion, 2006). Print.

— Severin, Timothy, *In Search of Moby Dick: the Quest for the White Whale* (New York: Basic, 2000). Print.

— Thomas, Keith Vivian, *Man and the Natural World: Changing Attitudes in England, 1500–1800* (London: Allen Lane, 1983). Print.

— Warner, Marina, *Six Myths of Our Time: Little Angels, Little Monsters, Beautiful Beasts, and More* (New York: Vintage, 1995). Print.

— Whitehead, Hal, *Sperm Whales: Social Evolution in the Ocean* (Chicago: University of Chicago Press, 2003). Print.

— Williams, Heathcote, *Whale Nation* (New York: Harmony, 1988). Print.

[LEFT] *Museum Of Extinction*. 2010.
Barrels, gold, cast narwhal tusks
and wax hearts.

[ABOVE] *Doubloon*, 2011, all the
gold I ever owned except my
wedding ring.

[RIGHT] *Weapons of Mass Extinction*.
2010–11. Found tope, bird wings,
& crustacean shells.

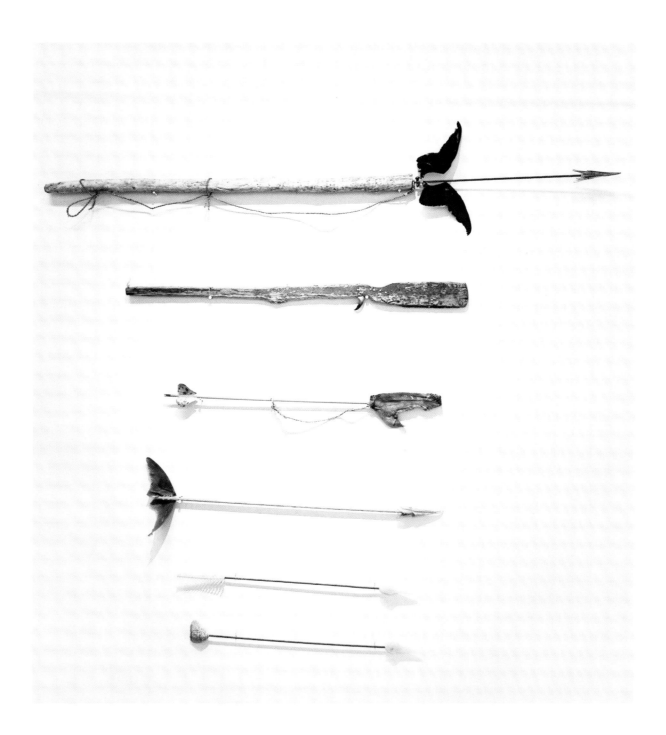

*Whether Leviathan can long endure so wide a chase,
and so remorseless a havoc; whether he must not at last be
exterminated from the waters, and the last whale, like the
last man, smoke his last pipe, and then himself
evaporate in the final puff.*

82–83

Photo-Shoot. 2010. Wax, hair, crustacean claws, lens, pewter.

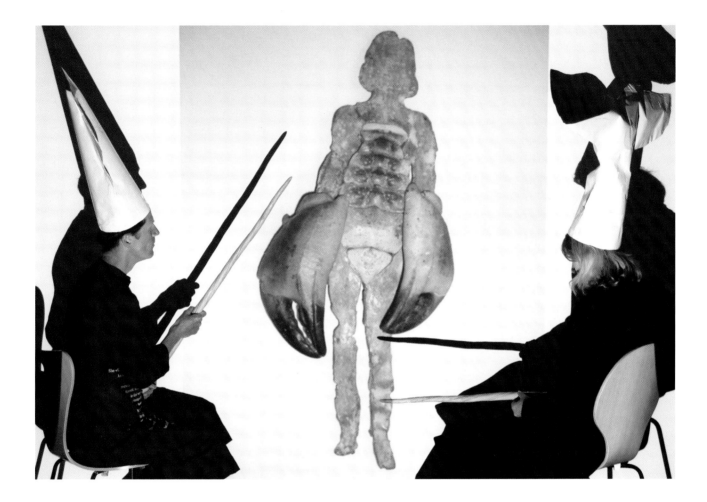

Dominion DVD film still. 2009.

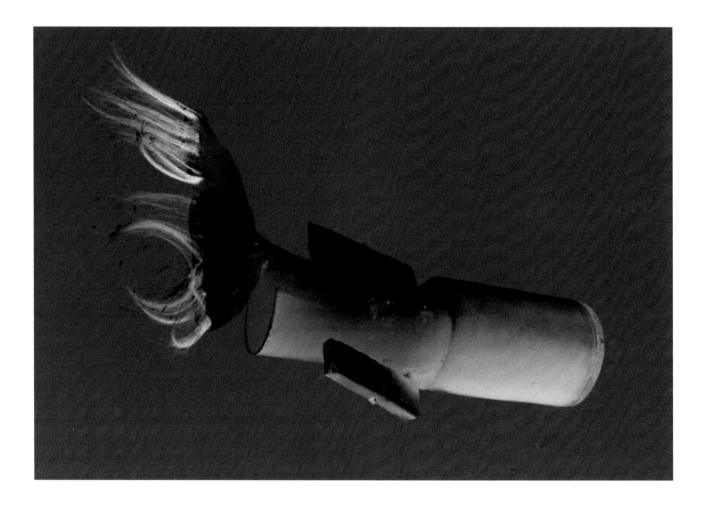

[ABOVE] *Hub Whale*. 2009. Wax, hair, mirror, glass, cuttlefish.
[RIGHT] *Specksynder*. 2008. Giclee print.

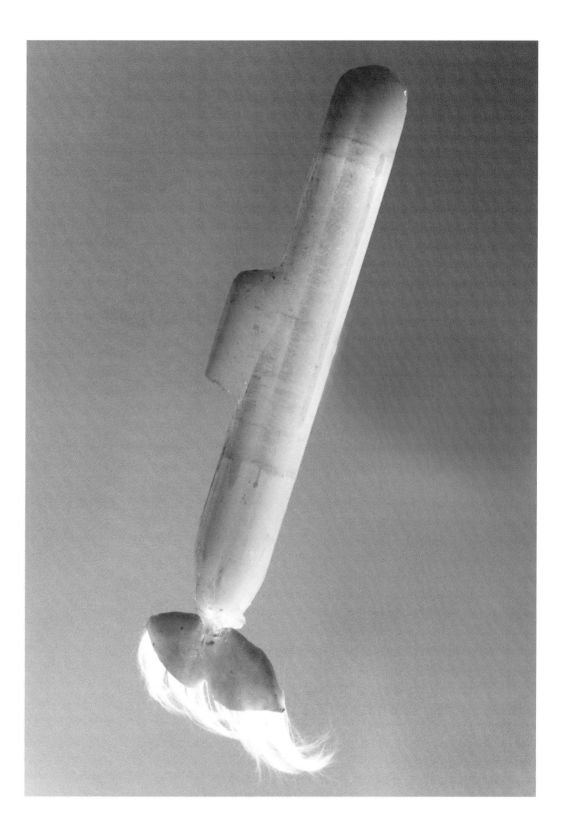

Albatross Chick, Midway Gyre. 2009. Chris Jordon.

DOMINION IN ART AND SCIENCE
Marine scientist Ruth Leeney in conversation with
artist Angela Cockayne

Plymouth, February 2011

In her book, *Art and Science*, Sian Ede describes how contemporary scientists often talk about beauty and elegance, rarefied words which contemporary artists tend not to use. Yet that sensibility may also converge, for instance, in the photographs of Chris Jordan, which depict the carcasses of albatross chicks that have consumed plastic debris on islands hundreds of miles from human habitation. These disturbing images could be described as horrifically beautiful; and yet they look as if an artist's hand had arranged them.

Many artists working today choose to work with science: from Wim Delvoye's *Cloaca*, a machine that performs the basic human function of digestion, to Thomas Grunfeld's hybrid creatures, from Mark Dion's taxidermied installations to Eduardo Kac's transgenic Day-Glo GFP Bunny. All are made in response to scientific investigation. In *Dominion*, these worlds converge; in a conversation sparked off by the exhibition and its symposium, marine scientist Ruth Leeney and artist Angela Cockayne discuss this new frontier.

Angela Cockayne The boundaries between contemporary art practice and science increasingly seem to cross over. Through multiple perspectives and theoretical discourse, they seem to offer us new dialogues between disciplines. Although one may be based on empirical evidence and rational hypothesis, both science and art come from a similar place, that of daydreaming. Both seem to offer a visualisation, abstraction and imagining through invention, creativity, and experimentation to present alternative ways of seeing. How do you see the links between art and science?

Ruth Leeney So much of what scientists work on and unearth remains within the scientific 'ivory tower'. But for scientists who want their work to have meaning in the real world, to impact our lives and perhaps to inspire a change for the better, communication of the findings of research is paramount. We have to make our work accessible to everyone, translate the dry, scientific language and put it back into the context from whence it came – that of living creatures and ecosystems.

To my mind, this is where art can play a key role – in making scientific findings accessible to non-scientists. By educating people about what we have learned through research, we can raise awareness and bring about a change in the way we, humankind, live and the impact we have on this earth and its other inhabitants.

Science all too easily separates humanity from 'the rest' of the world – we are the investigators, the observers, and the species which considers itself able to control its environment. As scientists, we are taught to separate ourselves from our subjects and observe them impartially, without emotion or involvement. But through artistic expression of our observations of, links with and emotions sparked by the natural world, we can be drawn back in to the picture, recognising once again that we are part of the continuity, which is the natural world. It is good, essential even, that we are reminded that we are not separate from nature, and that any wound we inflict upon the natural world, we inflict upon ourselves. We cannot survive without it, both through the ecosystem services it provides us, and through the solace and joy it gives.

In truth, I see there being a need for greater overlap between art and science. Certainly, in my role as a scientist, I see too little overlap or collaboration with artists. Through many creative media, science has the opportunity to reach many more people and spark their interest. This may be as simple as interpretive boards providing information to passers-by on a special natural environment, or addressing specific behaviours and attitudes towards elements of nature through film, exhibitions and books such as this.

AC As a scientist working in marine conservation, I'm intrigued by your identification with *The Whale and Squid* piece in the exhibition. It's made from plastic tampon applicators, found floating at sea, presented under a glass dome. At sea they just look like marine food floating on the surface, and are consumed by birds, fish and mammals.

RL The insidious permeation of plastics into every element of our own lives, and the spill over of that, too, impacts upon the rest of the natural world, is one which I am reminded of daily, and *The Whale and Squid* piece epitomises just that. Nothing that we do is without consequence. A simple idea, designed for human convenience, has come to blight beaches and contribute to the death of many marine organisms. It is ironic that a piece of plastic, be it a plastic shopping bag or part of a tampon, with such insignificance and so short a lifespan in a person's existence, does in fact persist and can have a powerfully negative impact elsewhere, by causing unnecessary death.

I have seen myriad pieces of plastic and other human-made materials afloat on the sea, encircling and constricting the necks of seals, entangling the tails and fins of whales, embedded in the skin and, like some parasite, even inside the stomachs of turtles and dolphins. Instinctively, these images look wrong to all of us; there is a discord between the black, smooth skin of a whale and a frayed, lurid-green polypropylene rope. But beyond that instinct, we can see the result of this disharmony: the death or disfigurement of so many marine species. Even these supposedly benevolent items we have created have become weapons against life in the seas.

AC If we are seeing such evidence of human consumption and pollution at this level, like the marine-debris raft of plastic particles supposedly as big as Texas floating in the Mid-Pacific, or Hawaiian atolls whose sandy shores have been replaced by plastic granules, surely it must be having a huge impact down the food chain at a microscopic level?

RL It most certainly is. There are so many things that we do not yet know, such as what the impact of microscopic plastic particulates can have on the health and wellbeing of ourselves and other living things. The Great Pacific Garbage Patch, the aggregation of particulate plastics in the Pacific Ocean, is a symbol of a much more widespread problem throughout all the oceans of the world. And just because we do not yet know what the negative effects might be of such materials pervading the marine environment and, eventually, our bodies, does not mean we should ignore the problem. There are so many things that we do not yet know, such as what impact microscopic plastic particulates can have on the health and well-being of ourselves and other living things. These tiny fragments of plastics are being found in all the oceans of the world. As plastics physically break down into smaller and smaller pieces, they become invisible to us but are nonetheless still present and have not become biodegraded. The pieces, confetti-sized or smaller, can then be ingested by fish and other marine organisms and thereby become integrated into every part of the food chain. They will, there-

Squid and Whale. 2010. Tampon applicators found on Cornish beaches.

Tampon applicator, Provincetown Beach. 2011
Amniohooks, found on North Cornish Beaches. 2000–11
Helium balloon floating at sea. Ruth Leeney. 2009

fore, make their way back to us at some point, if we consume seafood. Thus, our actions come full circle.

AC I was horrified recently when a sperm whale was washed up in the Mediterranean, the necropsy revealed that its stomach contained an array of plastic supermarket bags. I guess these must look like squid – their main source of food - when floating underwater. Ironically, ingesting them caused the whale, like the albatross chicks, to die of starvation. The Whale and Dolphin Conservation Society have just published data of a Minke whale stranding in France. Its stomach contained 800kgs of plastic including English supermarket bags.

RL It is horrific. We produce an estimated hundred million tons of plastics every year, and most of that is not recycled. Where do we expect it all to go? Stomach contents of many dead stranded marine animals, including not only sperm whales but other whale species as well as sharks, dolphins and seabirds, have been found to contain plastic bags and myriad other plastic and synthetic items. The endangered leatherback turtle is especially vulnerable because floating plastic bags likely resemble the turtles' main food source, jellyfish. The plastic cannot be digested and 'fills' the stomachs of these animals, preventing them from feeding and thus causing death by starvation. It is a horrible fate and a terrible waste of life in our already-depleted seas.

AC Working on the *Dominion* project, I'm interested in the whale as a metaphor and as an emblem of ecological threat. *Moby-Dick* seems to unite to unite both of these and, at the same time, highlight the self-destructive nature of *Homo sapiens*. I do not want to finger wag at the viewer; I'm implicated in the problem, too. But I think we need a paradigm shift. We need to ask not so much as what the whale can do for us, but what we can do for the whale. If we protect the whale's environment, we protect biodiversity and ourselves. How do you see our dominion of the whale?

RL In conservation science, the term 'flagship species' is often used these days for certain animals (such as whales, but also tigers, elephants, etc.) which can serve as the poster child for their environment, ensuring that by their protection, the ecosystem in which they live, including all other species (which may not capture the imagination as much as the whale) will also be protected. And indeed, in protecting marine biodiversity, we are protecting resources, which benefit humankind enormously. Such 'ecosystem services' provided by the marine environment may be as obvious as fish stocks, which provide us with food, or more complex like the absorption of carbon dioxide, one of the main gases which causes global warming, in the oceans. There are likely many other such 'services' that the ocean provides, enabling life on earth as we know it, which we have yet to understand or describe. Thus, efforts to protect and conserve whales are hopefully a powerful step towards protecting the oceans as a whole.

And so, to our 'dominion' of the whale. I am constantly amazed at how whales and dolphins fascinate so many people, far beyond the realm of coastal communities and lovers of the sea. This fascination, attraction even, has supported the transition from whaling to whale-watching across the planet and persists despite, or perhaps because of, the completely alien nature of these creatures. In some respects they are so foreign to us – devoid of the four limbs of our fellow land-dwelling mammals, spending long periods underwater in a world we barely understand and travelling distances unimaginable to us. And yet, there are elements of the whale that forge a connection – their use of complex language, their intelligence, perhaps even their apparent exuberance and ability to have 'fun'. So, I would contest that it is the whale that holds dominion over us. Despite the centuries of slaughter. Despite the cruelty we have imposed. Despite our disregard for their environment. We have been reliant, for oil, for baleen, but more recently we are simply bewitched. Perhaps it is the whale's ability to connect us with a wild freedom we barely remember in this crowded, built-up world we have created. As Douglas Adams put it:

Man has always assumed that he was more intelligent than dolphins because he had achieved so much ... the wheel, New York, wars and so on ... while all the dolphins had ever done was muck about in the water having a good time. But conversely, the dolphins had always believed that they were far more intelligent than man ... for precisely the same reason.

I would be inclined to agree with the dolphins!

AC It's for these reasons, and after seeing Chris Jordan's images, that I have become very conscious in my use of materials. As far as possible, I use natural organic material, much of which I find washed up

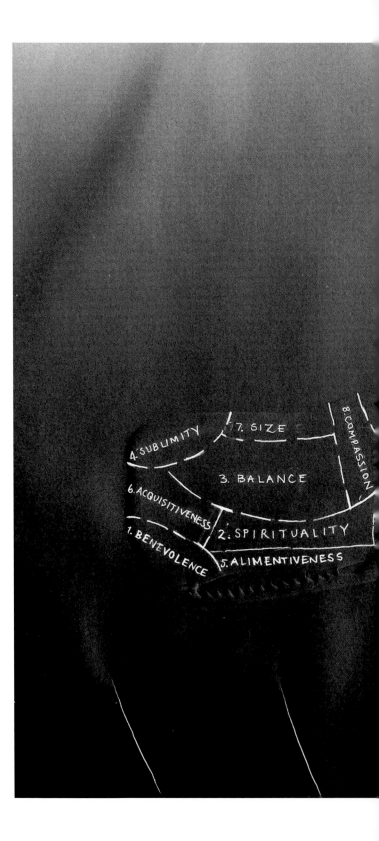

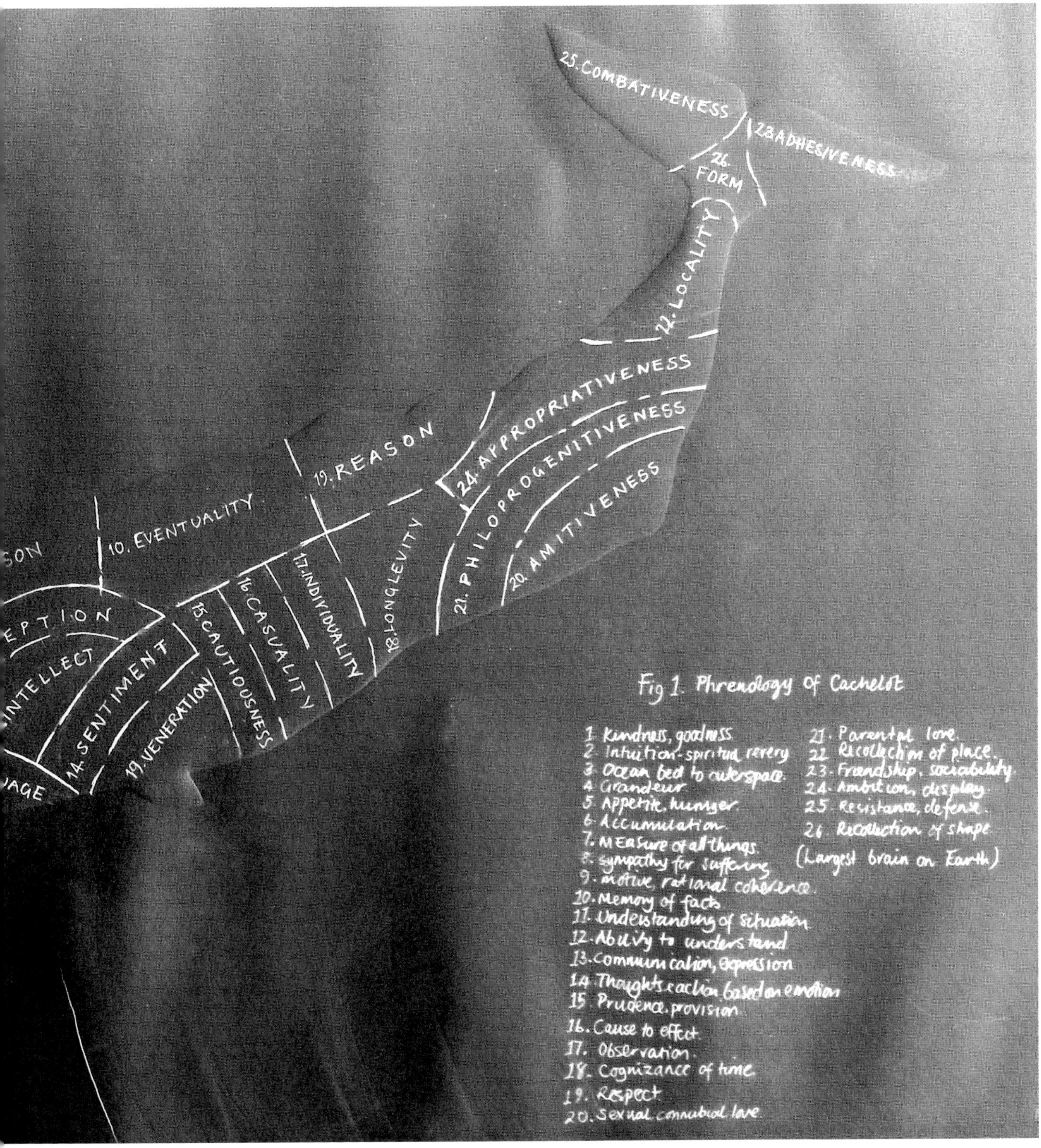

Fig 1. Phrenology of Cachelot

25. COMBATIVENESS
23. ADHESIVENESS
26. FORM
22. LOCALITY
24. APPROPRIATIVENESS
19. REASON
21. PHILOPROGENITIVENESS
20. AMITIVENESS
10. EVENTUALITY
18. LONGEVITY
17. INDIVIDUALITY
16. CASUALITY
15. CAUTIOUSNESS
...EPTION
...INTELLECT
14. SENTIMENT
13. VENERATION
...SON
...AGE

1. kindness, goodness
2. Intuition - spiritual revery
3. Ocean bed to outerspace
4. Grandeur
5. Appetite, hunger
6. Accumulation
7. Measure of all things
8. sympathy for suffering
9. motive, rational coherence
10. Memory of facts
11. Understanding of situation
12. Ability to understand
13. Communication, expression
14. Thoughts, action based on emotion
15. Prudence, provision
16. Cause to effect
17. Observation
18. Cognizance of time
19. Respect
20. Sexual connubial love

21. Parental love
22. Recollection of place
23. friendship, sociability
24. Ambition, display
25. Resistance, defense
26. Recollection of shape

(Largest brain on Earth)

on the liminal space of shorelines. I've become almost evangelical in my research and promotion of eco resin – a biodegradable material that can be composted. We have to take sustainability for granted, but companies have to become more environmentally, globally responsible. Designing products which have inbuilt obsolescence needs to be addressed. At very least, they should be made from biodegradable materials so they do not pollute our earth and oceans. Offering limited facility design and the need for constant upgrades may be good for short-term financial gain, but it comes with a huge environmental price tag. Preservation of our oceans is vital, 80% of all life on earth is found under or on the ocean surface. Global warming, ocean acidification, pollution, over-harvesting and rising sea temperatures threaten not only marine biodiversity, but filtration for the air we breathe. Our dominion of the oceans may lead to catastrophic loss of not only the species that inhabit them but also ourselves? I know you have spent months observing wildlife in the ocean. What environmental problems do you see facing marine life in the ocean?

RL We all need to become more aware of how much plastic is involved in our everyday lives. We need to think back to the previous century, before foodstuffs and drinks were packaged in plastic, and before we had access to so many different 'lifestyle' items like laptop computers and MP3 players. We need to start demanding alternatives in the way we source our food and in the way the things we buy are made and packaged. We have to ask our politicians to bring about changes in policy that will promote more sustainable practices. It doesn't have to be difficult but until it becomes a mainstream practice, it will be more expensive and more difficult for the few companies who do follow these practices. Alternatives to plastic are available – for example, a corn fibreplant fibres can be used to make soft drinks bottles. Plastics can be recycled. But eventually, it will also come down to every individual asking themselves how much they really need to consume; whether they truly need that new gadget every year or two.

The use of plastics and other materials is a problem not just for our oceans, but also for the planet as a whole. At some point all our discarded things will be jostling for space on land with a growing human population, and all the while, the sea will be encroaching on that same land space as sea levels rise.

The effects of rising sea temperatures and ocean acidification will also pose huge challenges for marine life. As oceans absorb increased levels of carbon dioxide from the atmosphere, they become more acidic. Changing the chemistry of our seas is no insignificant matter, and will likely impact in ways we cannot yet imagine. One of the main concerns is for calcifying organisms – small marine animals that produce calcium carbonate shells. A more acidic environment will dissolve their shells and thus may diminish populations of these small animals, which of course form an important part of the marine food web. Rising sea temperatures and changes in oceanic currents will also change the patterns of productivity in our oceans – where fish, krill and other organisms become concentrated and thus where species like whales, dolphins, sharks and sea birds aggregate to find food.

AC It seems to me that working across the different disciplines of science, art, literature and music, opens up new visions and possibility, greater capacity for exciting dialogue between research communities, but also for a wider audience participation.

In the plenary after the symposium many interesting issues were discussed. What do you see as a way forward?

RL The plenary session highlighted the importance of whales to humankind, historically, culturally, and even spiritually. Acknowledging this importance is a great step along the path towards examining the direction our own lives are taking and asking ourselves, is that direction one which respects the whale and its world? That world is, after all, one which sustains our existence also. The way forward, then, might be to ask ourselves how we can bring our regard for the whale and the oceans into our everyday lives. We have made significant changes in our attitudes to whales in the past – from fearing the mighty and mystical Leviathan to viewing whales as our prey, a resource to be exploited, and from there to the 1986 moratorium on commercial whaling and a more benevolent appreciation of these creatures. Can we take the next step, looking not only at the whale but also at ourselves, seeing the impact we each have on the world we share with the whale and trying to make a positive change?

AC I agree with your analysis as all too often we speak to our own exclusive communities: scientists to scientists, artists to artists. What

I find fascinating is how the whale can occupy such a hold on our collective imagination; and with that, the knowledge that we need to effect change if we are to protect our environment – and ultimately ourselves. The difficulty comes when we realise that the consequence of change needed is long term. In his book, *Gray's Anatomy*, the philosopher John Gray describes how, by accepting that we are flawed in our irresponsible attitude to resources and the natural world, we need to act long term. This is all the more difficult to do when government and global business operate on short-term goals. 'Science and technology have given us power', he writes. But perhaps poetry, faith and myth may be more realistic guides to life.

This notion is also beautifully echoed in Cornelia Parker's extraordinary interview with Noam Chomsky in *Chomskian Abstract*, in which the artist and philosopher steps quite out of context, discussing his thoughts on the potential environmental disaster which threatens our world if we choose to ignore climate change. In this compelling interview, projected on a gallery wall as a portrait and huge talking head, Chomsky suggests that in order to survive we need to act long term – which is not always in our own personal interests – and how capitalism compels us to work and take more than we need.

It seems to me that many other species appear to act more responsibly than man: the honeybee, the meerkat and the sperm whale: three very diverse creatures, yet ones which seem to have a better grasp on social evolution and the ability to behave unselfishly for the greater good. Somehow we need to implement change in the way we consume on an international scale and find a way to co-exist with other species, and celebrate our precious natural resources in the hope of making conservation and sustainability globally acceptable and paramount in our consumption, if we are not to follow Melville's prophetic vision of our propensity toward self-destruction.

RL Most of us walk better than we swim, spend more time on land than in or under water, and are better equipped to perceive the effects our actions have on the terrestrial environment around us than to understand the dynamics of marine ecosystems. We can therefore tend to separate ourselves and our *terra firma* from that which covers over seventy per cent of our planet, forgetting that the unexplored, unfathomable oceans play a key role in how our planet functions, from governing weather patterns and climate to supplying us with food. Whilst we may no longer consider the sea as a limitless resource to support humankind and absorb, unnoticed, humanity's insults, the full understanding of what a shift in the biology, chemistry and oceanography of the oceans will mean for the planet, and thus for each one of us, is yet to come.

Sources
— Ede, Siân. *Art and Science*. (London: I. B. Tauris, 2005). Print.
— Gray, John. *Gray's Anatomy: Selected Writings*. (London: Penguin, 2010). Print.
— Heartney, Eleanor. *Art & Today*. (London: Phaidon, 2008). Print.
— Leonard, Annie, and Ariane Conrad. *The Story of Stuff: How Our Obsession with Stuff Is Trashing the Planet, -and a Vision for Change*. (New York: Free, 2010).
— Cornelia Parker *Chomskian Abstract* - 2007.03.09 . Film
— Wilson, Edward O. *The Diversity of Life*. (New York : London: W. W. Norton &, 1992). Print.
— James M. and Rogers, Donald B. *Marine Debris : Sources, Impacts, and Solutions*. (Springer-Verlag New York Inc. 1997). Print
— http://www.genomenewsnetwork.org/articles/03_02/bunny_art.shtml
— http://www.bbc.co.uk/news/world-asia-pacific-12994785
— http://www.tate.org.uk/tateetc/issue20/aiweiwei.htm
— http://www.chrisjordan.com/gallery/midway/#CF000313%2018x24
— https://www.coastalstudies.org/whats-new/8-20-10.htm

S T R A N

Men's Troubles June 2006

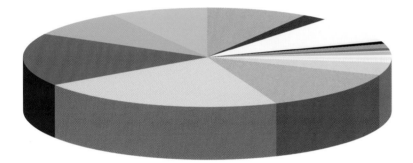

Personal Health

Self Esteem

Ageing

Excessive Eating

Excessive Drinking

Natural Disasters

House Fires

Floods

Robbery

Personal Attack

Terrorist Attack

Family Health

Family Behaviour

Sexual Discrimination

Racial Discrimination

Global Warming

World Poverty

Money

Other

[RIGHT] *Slumber*. 2006. Duvet whales made in correlation to data on men's worries above.

FOR THOSE IS PERIL: MUSIC AND HERMAN MELVILLE
A composer's view, Nick Atkinson

In September 2009 I composed the soundtrack for a film by Angela Cockayne and Philip Hoare entitled *Dominion*. This turned out to be the beginning of a journey. I subsequently developed the score and added two new sections of music for a live performance accompanying a projection of a more recent film by Angela: *Rachel's Orphan*. The new piece was performed by violinist Lorna Osbon and myself at the Peninsular Arts Whale Conference at Plymouth University in February 2011. This paper was presented at the conference as an immediate sequel to the live performance.

I was invited 'as a composer' to contribute a paper relating to whales or *Moby-Dick*. The conference brought together scientists, visual artists, writers and musicians, and I accepted, attracted by the spirit of interdisciplinarity and collaboration. I also felt personally drawn to the subject, having lived for a year in Boston. Subsequently I regretted it. The other contributors seemed to work in media or subjects where direct involvement with 'real' things is habitual: Angela's work deals with recognisable images of marine life; Anthony Caleshu's poetry locates itself in Melville's world; scientists deal with the stuff of nature itself; against this, what can a composer have to say about whales or *Moby-Dick*? Instrumental music would appear to have little to do with things outside its own closed domain of pitches, durations and musical structures.

I re-read *Moby-Dick*. I was again disturbed by Ishmael's imagining of the white whale 'like a snow hill in the air',[1] which chimed with childhood nightmares of shapes I could never delineate. I also re-read a book I liked as much as *Moby-Dick* when I discovered it years ago: *Call Me Ishmael* by Charles Olson, an improvisation by a poet on Melville's novel. In the end I decided that writing the music for *Dominion* and developing it into the 'live' version that accompanied *Rachel's Orphan* was itself a form of paper. The best course would be to use words to explore issues that arose from the composing.

The conference audiences were a broad mix of interests and expertise so I could not assume any knowledge of music. Music examples were audio recordings without scores and I mostly avoided the use of specialist terminology. In adapting the paper for print I have added two examples in score, though the issues discussed remain the same. I apologise for the occasional reference to heard music that was played in the presentation but cannot be reproduced in the paper, such as the discussion of different choirs' interpretations of southern American hymnody. I hope that readers may discover these recordings for themselves if so motivated.

In order to write music that looks for a relationship with extra-musical objects like whales, a composer has at least three choices.

1. Music can engage concretely, by using material derived from the subject. In this case it would mean referencing the sounds made by whales – and perhaps, as suggested by Hal Whitehead in his keynote speech for the conference, using the opportunity to research into possible meanings in the patterns and acoustic properties of the sounds.

2. Music can engage conceptually: it can follow a scheme that mirrors the subject in some way. This could involve picking up on processes or structures connected with whales, such as transitions from shallows to depths.

3. Finally, music can engage emotionally … it can relate to, drive, or intensify our reaction to the film. It can try to activate our emotional regard for the whale with a view to turning that into committed action of some kind.

The film score for *Dominion* takes the third, the 'emotional' approach. The intention (though not necessarily the effect) was to create and preserve mood in order to allow Angela's images and objects to disclose themselves in all their poignancy. If this is successful (and only the listener can judge) then the composer can feel him/herself to have 'engaged'.

In the *Rachel's Orphan* performance version, on the other hand, it became at times a matter of the second, the conceptual approach. In the absence of the heard music it would be fruitless to discuss this in more detail, other than to comment that the score is structured as a descent into depths and one section follows up a concern with whiteness: 'the whiteness of the whale that above all things appalled me' as Ishmael says in *Moby-Dick*.

So far, not much to hang a paper from. However, there is a more interesting, and, for the musician looking for a way into Melville, a more useful, aspect of the composing of *Rachel's Orphan*. One section uses fragments of my thirteen-year-old daughter Jess singing the hymn *Eternal Father Strong to Save* – the so-called 'navy hymn' (a fact that she is now slightly embarrassed to be reminded of …). The choice of tune was Angela's suggestion, and initially we looked to using recordings of choirs or military bands. In the end the issue of intellectual property deterred us, and it figures as it now does: sung by a teenager, fragmented and reordered, and with no words.

Why is the use of a hymn so significant for a discussion of Herman Melville? To answer this we can ask another obvious question in a paper where a musician looks at *Moby-Dick*. Alongside the major literary works of nineteenth-century Europe there are equally strong contemporary compositions in music: *Mansfield Park* and *Fidelio*; *Middlemarch* and *Aida*; *Jude the Obscure* and *Ein Heldenleben*. When we turn to *Moby-Dick* and its New England context, and we look for the American equivalents in music … well, where are they? What are the symphonic parallels to the Great American Novel? We search in vain for American concert or operatic music before 1900 that has the depth and originality of *Moby-Dick*. There are some good compositions (by Edward MacDowell for example) but not of the stature of Melville's novel. If, that is, by 'stature' we mean not size but authenticity, being somehow vitally relevant to our lives over a century and a half later.

To find that authenticity in nineteenth-century America we have to turn to a smaller form. There flourished from the late eighteenth century onwards in New England a strong culture of hymnody. It's an interesting question whether this music is classical or folk in identity. It has been described as classical in origin, folk in usage, and this is probably as good a fence-sitting position as any. It is classical – as created by named and classically trained composers, written down in music notation, using artifices such as fugue, and framed in church-music forms derived from the English Protestant tradition. It is folk

– as later learned and culturally digested by oral teaching (often in a call-and-response format), using non-classical methods of reading like shape-notes,[2] and becoming so embedded in folk-culture that later hymns can use bits of earlier hymns borrowed and slipped in as and when needed.[3] This music, though in its origin somewhat earlier than Melville, would, as a continuing tradition and part of the bedrock of north-eastern United States culture, have been a significant presence in his world.

I said this is where authenticity lies. What do I mean by authenticity? Early American hymnody is in many ways unsophisticated, but there is an element of integrity, of conviction that is often powerful. Sometimes this takes the form of energetic defiance, such as the famous *Chester* by William Billings of Boston[4] that became a patriotic anthem for the colonial armies in the War of Independence.

Example 1.

At other times the power is more complex and expressively moving. Take, for instance, the first seven measures of Daniel Read's *Mortality*.[5] The lines of the text are structured thus:

> Death like an overflowing stream
> Sweeps us away; our life's a dream.

In the music, however, the end of the first line carries on without a break into the second, and the gap is in the middle of line two. The music goes with the text's punctuation rather than its line disposition. As a result, at the words 'sweeps us away' the music propels us over the apparent end of the phrase, aided by the stretching of the chord on 'stream' and the fact that singing the phrase takes a lot of breath. The next phrase is short by contrast.

Example 2.

This attention to detail and sensitivity to the text, this creation of a powerful moment fixed by music notation can be said to be classical in outlook. And in this case it is authentic in Heidegger's sense of the word, as taking on and making real through the power of music an awareness of the ever-present possibility of death.

Above all, these hymns and anthems had a purpose in strengthening the soul against the dangers of a still partly unknown environment, spiritual as well as physical. Early American hymnody, since the *Bay Psalm Book* of the Pilgrim Fathers, had been weaponry in the war against the not-understood. If we move forward in time to the man many regard as America's first major symphonic composer we can see this more overtly.

The opening of Charles Ives' 4th Symphony, dating from the years of World War I, presents us with a clear and dynamic spiritual programme. We hear three events: a widening gap between top and bottom lines of the orchestra opens up a large space; in this expanse we hear distant sounds trembling in flute, harp and tremolo violins; then the chorus sings a well-known American hymn: *Watchman Tell us of the Night* by Lowell Mason. The inference is clear: only vigilance – helped by singing as an act of communal security – can guard against the perils of the unknown spaces around us. In the symphony's second movement, a sense of vastness is created by a wide and dense polyphony of orchestral lines that borders on the chaotic.

Space, and our response to it, is the issue for Ives, and it is of course a preoccupation in Olson's book about Melville's book. Olson begins:

> I take SPACE to be the central fact to man born in America ...
> I spell it large because it comes large here. Large, and without
> mercy.[6]

Space ... and the corresponding whiteness of the whale, experienced but not delineated, that so appals Ishmael ...

In Ives the position is ambiguous, as it is for Ishmael. The space, the 'snow hill in the air' and its lack of form, the suggestions of chaos, are frightening – but they are also to be welcomed for their freedom and fascination. Take for instance the first of Ives' *Three Harvest Home Chorales*. We hear an initial verse where the choir sings a clearly structured and measured melody with a subdued and rhythmically independent double bass accompaniment. By the third and final verse the melody has been swamped by a complex fabric of lines and accretions that are only suggested in the original bass part. The centrifugal forces of the music threaten to destroy it, and for Ives they are to be welcomed for their unleashing of energy and the absence of boundaries.

From where did he derive this fascination with something that seems like chaos? For answer we can return to hymnody and compare two recorded versions of the same shape-note hymn called *Wondrous Love* from the collection Southern Harmony published in South Carolina in 1835 (though the anonymous folk melody doubtless predates this).

Version one is by the modern New York-based vocal group Anonymous 4. It is rhythmically tight, energetic, agile – and fast.[7] However, what Ives (and possibly Melville) would have encountered at church or at a Revivalist camp meeting would have been more like another version of *Wondrous Love* recorded in eastern Tennessee in the 1950s.[8] Here the music is slow and there are obvious divergences in intonation by individual singers. This is a small choir; multiply these variations by the hundreds of participants in one of the camp-meetings that Ives would have heard, and the composer's love of wild polyphony falls into place. Ives himself describes the singing at outdoor camp-meetings in Redding, Connecticut:

I remember how the great waves of sound used to come through the trees when things like *Beulah Land*, *Woodworth*, *The Shining Shore*, *Nettleton*, *Nearer my God to Thee*, *In the Sweet Bye and Bye* and the like were sung by a thousand 'let-out' souls.[9]

Or this, from an earlier nineteenth-century eyewitness:

The immediate din was tremendous; at a hundred yards it was beautiful; at a distance of a half a mile it was magnificent.[10]

For Ives the apparent disorder meant conviction, passion and energy. He refers this back to his father, George Ives:

Once, when father was asked 'How can you stand it to hear old John Bell … bellow off-key the way he does at camp-meetings?' his answer was: 'Old John is a supreme musician. Look into his face and hear the music of the ages. Don't pay too much attention to the sounds. If you do, you may miss the music.'[11]

In camp-meeting music there is an interesting balance between the linear and the harmonic. The emphasis in performance is probably more on how the line feels to sing than on the harmony it makes when sounding with other lines (something of an irony when we consider the titles of many of these hymn books: *Southern Harmony*, *Harmony of Maine*, *Continental Harmony*). The unbridled individual melody expresses the personal truth of the singer's own conviction and feeling. The paradox, of course, is that the music grows out of a strong sense of community and its potential for emotional power can only be realised in the social act of singing together. This is harmony in the communal and spiritual sense: Ives himself, in a more conservative moment, refers to 'the common triad of the New England homestead'.[12] But the individual energy of so many singers is a constant centrifugal force that threatens to pull the music apart.[13]

So for Ives, as for Ishmael, the formlessness of the 'snow hill in the air' is exciting and fulfilling as well as intimidating. To return to Olson's concern with space and with how we respond:

Some men ride on such space, others have to fasten themselves like a tent stake to survive. As I see it Poe dug in and Melville mounted. They are the alternatives.[14]

Ives, that singular combination of revolutionary and New England conservative, did both.

To finish: in using *Eternal Father, Strong to Save* I became interested in the status of the hymn-form as an icon of protection against the forces of nature – which it is in this particular hymn for countless travellers upon the ocean. The hymn is a sign of our old fear of our environment. And of Ishmael's apprehension at what lay at the end of the voyage of the *Pequod*.

Text Sources
— Chase, G., *America's Music* (New York: McGraw-Hull Book Co.,1966).
— Cowell, H. and S. Cowell, *Charles Ives and his Music* (Oxford: Oxford University Press, 1969).
— Ives, C., *Essays Before a Sonata* (London: Calder and Boyars, 1969).
— Kingman, D., *American Music: A Panorama* (New York: Schirmer Books, 1979).
— Olson, C., *Call Me Ishmael* (San Francisco: City Lights Books, 1986).
— Perlis, V., *Charles Ives Remembered: An Oral History* (New York: Norton, 1974).
— White, B. and E. King, *Original Sacred Harp* (Bremen: Sacred Harp Publishing Co., 1971).

Audio Sources
— Anonymous 4, *American Angels: Songs of Hope, Redemption, & Glory* (Harmonia Mundi, 2003).
— Old Harp Singers of Eastern Tennessee, *Old Harp Singing* (New York: Folkways Records, 1951).
— Old Sturbridge Singers, *New England Harmony* (New York: Folkways Records, 1964).

Source Notes
1 The 'snow hill' quotation from *Moby-Dick* is in my rather yellowing Jonathan Cape 1923 [?] edition, to be found on page 12.
2 Shape-note notation was a method of music scoring where the pitch of a note is designated by shape as well as position on a line. This enabled it to be read by people who are musically untrained: the singer would identify the pitch of a note in fa-so-la (the contemporary American equivalent of do-re-mi) from its shape. The system was particularly prevalent in the South, and is still sometimes used today.
3 D. Kingman, *American Music: A Panorama* (New York: Schirmer Books, 1979), p. 162.
4 William Billings (1746–1800) was probably the most highly regarded composer of this generation – a fact that didn't prevent him from living much of his life in extreme poverty. His 'day jobs' included tanning, cleaning streets and rounding up stray pigs. Despite this, between 1770 and 1794 he produced five volumes

of vocal music containing many fine compositions that still occupy a prominent position in the repertoires of American choirs today. He is regarded by some as America's first significant composer.

5   Daniel Read (1757–1836) of Newhaven was more materially successful than Billings, though he still derived his income as much from store-keeping and the manufacture of combs as from music. Two volumes of hymns, anthems and 'fuging tunes' were issued in 1785 and 1793 and, like Billings, he is regarded as a major figure in the early New England hymn-writing movement. In the extract quoted, the melody is in the tenor part, and the top line is an embellishment – a scheme that characterised most of the four-part vocal music of this period.

6   C. Olson, *Call Me Ishmael* (San Francisco: City Lights Books, 1986), p.11.

7   Anonymous 4, *American Angels: Songs of Hope, Redemption, & Glory* (Harmonia Mundi, 2003).

8   Old Harp Singers of Eastern Tennessee, *Old Harp Singing* (New York: Folkways Records, 1951).

9   Quoted in H. Cowell and S. Cowell, *Charles Ives and his Music* (Oxford: Oxford University Press, 1969), pp. 23–4.

10 Samuel Asbury quoted in G. Chase, *America's Music* (New York: McGraw-Hull Book Co.,1966), p. 223.

11 Quoted in Cowell and Cowell, *Charles Ives and his Music*, p. 24.

12 C. Ives, *Essays Before a Sonata* (London: Calder and Boyars, 1969), p. 47.

13 For us now, and especially for classically trained musicians, the equation between polyphony and lack of form is an odd notion. We are more likely to see counterpoint, when learned by our music students, for example, as the epitome of musical order and rationality.

14 Olson, *Call Me Ishmael*, p. 11.

Yoke. 2009. Wood, chain, golden claws, jesmonite.

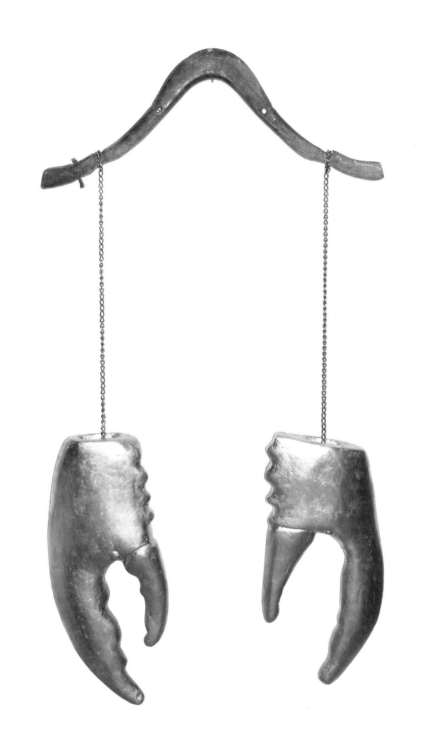

FAST TRAVEL
Alexis Kirke

Dominion launches on 21 January with *Fast Travel*, a new piece of music inspired by the exhibition. Composed by Alexis Kirke (Plymouth Marine Institute's composer-in-residence and member of the Interdisciplinary Centre for Computer Music Research) *Fast Travel* refers to the songs blue whales sing when they are moving fast and is a responsive piece between an artificially intelligent whale school and saxophone.

Fast Travel – Introduction
A composer was commissioned by the University of Plymouth to create computerised schools of intelligent surround-sound singing whales, to perform with a saxophonist. The piece was premiered at the opening of the 'Dominion' exhibition, 21 January 2011 in Plymouth. The artificially intelligent animals swam around an invisible virtual sea containing the audience and saxophonist who were all 'inside' the sound of the schools and the sea, surrounded by speakers. As whales swam they moved between speakers, and the schools sang to each other electronically, evolving new songs based on hearing each other in this 'sea'. The live saxophone – played by Andy Visser, a Death in Vegas collaborator – sounded over the ghostly artificial whale song, using a score by composer Alexis Kirke, and also heard live by the whales; interacting with and influencing their song – sometimes like another whale, sometimes like marine acoustic phenomena.

The piece was called *Fast Travel*, and this scientific term refers to the songs blue whales sing when they are moving fast rather than, for example, their 'feeding' songs. The fast travel calls come in repeated A–B pairs. The B songs were found by recent research to have the extraordinary property of perfect tuning to the key of C, having dropped a major third from the key of E in the last half-century, one reason hypothesised being man-made marine sounds. The performance is called *Fast Travel* not just because of this inspiration but because of the way it speeds up the evolution of the whales' song tuning. Fifty years is compressed down into the ten minutes as the audience time travel through the evolution of the underwater song. But the tuning evolution is driven here by the saxophone, rather than solely by other whales or man-made acoustic phenomena. The saxophone is audible to the whales, and influences their tunes through imitation and an effect i 6   ▶ 6   ▶ 100   ☒

spawn $1   remove   getinfo   A   rate $1   active $1

js fastTravel.js

artificial whales agents:

js awa.js 0

whale_e w0

js awa.js 1

whale_e w1

js awa.js 2

whale_e w2

js awa.js 3

whale_e w3

js awa.js 4

whale_e w4

js awa.js 5

whale_e w5

p otherSettings

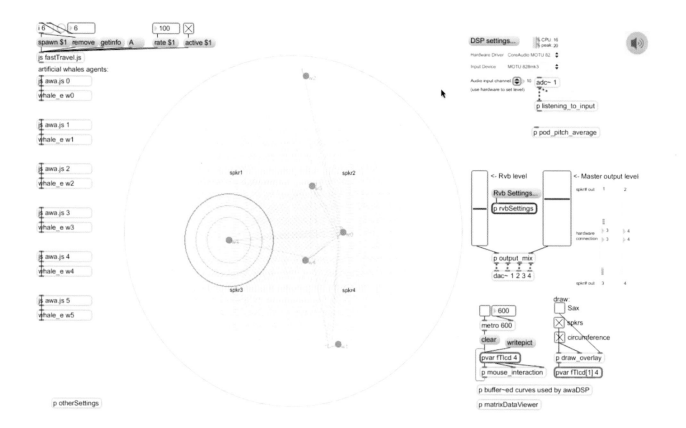

DSP settings...   CPU 16
                       peak 20

Hardware Driver   CoreAudio MOTU 82 ▲▼

Input Device   MOTU 828mk3   ▲▼

Audio input channel ▲▼ 10   adc~ 1
(use hardware to set level)

p listening_to_input

p pod_pitch_average

                <- Rvb level   <- Master output level

               Rvb Settings...   spkr# out   1   2

               p rvbSettings

                                       hardware   ▶ 3   ▶ 4
                                       connection ▶ 3   ▶ 4

               p output mix

               dac~ 1 2 3 4   spkr# out   3   4

                                        draw:
     ▶ 600   Sax
metro 600   ☒ spkrs
clear   writepict   ☒ circumference
pvar fTlcd 4   p draw_overlay
p mouse_interaction   pvar fTlcd[1] 4

p buffer~ed curves used by awaDSP

p matrixDataViewer

call 'masking'. Hence the saxophonist is able to use a score by Alexis to move the whales' songs into lower keys. Within this time whales communicate and learn tunes from each other too. The artificial whale schools are not limited to the deep calls of blue whales, but extended to include humpbacks, renowned for beautiful social singing.

Alexis Kirke, a member of the Interdisciplinary Centre for Computer Music Research at the University of Plymouth, is also Composer-in-Residence of the Plymouth Marine Institute. His most recent work to hit the national press was *Cloud Chamber*, in which subatomic particles from cosmic rays and radioactive material duetted live with a violinist. *Fast Travel* was his first marine-related piece and was commissioned by Peninsula Arts at the University of Plymouth. Alexis developed the idea for the piece and composed the saxophone part and whale song, collaborating with expert technologist Sam Freeman and Marine Mammal Biologist Dr Simon Ingram. The methods used in this piece have been inspired by research developed at the University's Interdisciplinary Centre for Computer Music Research.

Once the main performance of *Fast Travel* was over the whale schools were left swimming around the performance space, and the audience was invited to try out the microphone used by the saxophone and to influence the whales themselves.

Humpback whale song is incredibly beautiful, especially when heard echoing underwater by divers lucky enough to be near a school. Most of us will never get to swim amongst singing humpbacks. Also most of us will never get to hear the deep throbbing and subsonic blue whale song. Through the use of sound diffusion techniques in MAX/MSP and whale song modelling, it becomes possible to immerse the audience not only in an artificial whale environment, but also in a musical composition. The scored saxophone is audible to the whales, and influences their tunes through imitation. Although the majority of the saxophone music will be pre-scored, the behaviour of the artificial whales is not one hundred per cent predictable because of their complex interactions, and so the performance will be different each time. *Fast Travel* was commissioned by Peninsula Arts, University of Plymouth. The technologist is Samuel Freeman, University of Huddersfield; the Marine Mammal Consultant is Simon Ingram at the Marine Institute, University of Plymouth. As a result of the initiation of Fast Travel as an artistic project, a new project is being developed in the purely scientific arena for humpback whale modelling. This is an unusual example of an artistic project being the inspiration for a hard-science project, rather than the other way round.

References

— Oleson, E., J. Calambokidis, W. Burgess, M. McDonald, C. LeDuc and J. Hildebrand, 'Behavioral context of call production by eastern North Pacific blue whales, Columbia University', *Marine Ecology Progress Series*, 330 (2007), pp. 269–84.

— McDonald, M., J. Hildebrand and S. Wiggins, 'Increases in deep ocean ambient noise in the Northeast Pacific west of San Nicolas Island, California', *Journal of the Acoustical Society of America*, 120:2 (2006), pp. 711–18.

— Mercado III, E., L. Herman and A. Pack, 'Song copying by humpback whales: themes and variations', *Animal Cognition*, 8:2 (2005).

— McDonald, M., J. Hildebrand and S. Mesnick, 'Biogeographic characterization of blue whale song worldwide: using song to identify populations', *Journal of Cetacean Research and Management*, 8:1 (2006), pp. 55–65.

— Hoffman, M., N. Garfield and R. Bland, 'Frequency synchronization of blue whale calls near Pioneer Seamount', *Journal of the Acoustical Society of America*, 128:1 (2010), pp. 490–4.

— Payne, R. and S. McVay, 'Songs of humpback whales', *Science*, 173:3997 (1971).

— Wooldridge, M., *An Introduction to Multiagent Systems* (Chichester: John Wiley and Sons, 2004).

— Murray-Rust, D. and A. Smaill, 'Musical acts and musical agents', in *Proceedings of the Fifth Open Workshop of MUSICNETWORK* (Vienna, Austria, 2005).

— Baxter, J., G. Horn, and D. Leivers, 'Fly-by-agent: Controlling a pool of UAVs via a multi-agent system', in *Proceedings of the Twenty-seventh SGAI International Conference on Innovative Techniques and Applications of Artificial Intelligence (AI-2007)* (Cambridge, UK, 2007).

— Grimm, V. and S. F. Railsback, 'Agent-based models in ecology: patterns and alternative theories of adaptive behaviour', in F. Billari, T. Fent, A. Prskawetz and J. Sceffran (eds), *Agent-Based Computational Modelling: Applications in Demography, Social, Economic and Environmental Sciences* (Heidelberg: Physica-Verlag, 1995), pp. 139–52.

— Miranda, E., 'Emergent sound repertoires in virtual societies', *Computer Music Journal*, 26 (2002), pp. 77–90.

— Gong, T., Q. Zhang and H. Wu, 'Music evolution in a complex system of interacting agents', in *Proceedings of the 2005 IEEE Congress on Evolutionary Computation* (Edinburgh, UK, 2005).

— Dhar, P., I. Mohammad, K. Deb and J. Kim, 'A modified spectral modelling synthesis algorithm for whale sound', *International Journal of Computer Science and Network Security*, 10:9 (2010).

— Anwar, S., C. Jeanneret, L. Parrott and D. Marceau, 'Conceptualization and implementation of a multi-agent model to simulate whale-watching tours in the St Lawrence Estuary in Quebec, Canada', *Environmental Modelling & Software*, 22:12 (2007).

— Apple Corporation, Logic Studio (Logic Pro 9), 2009.

OF WHALES: IN PRINT, IN PAINT …
Anthony Caleshu

Of Whales: in Print, in Paint, in Sea, in Stars, in Coin, in House, in Margins (Salt, 2010)

In 1947, Charles Olson published *Call Me Ishmael*, his wonderfully unorthodox book of literary criticism on how Herman Melville composed *Moby-Dick*. Olson argues that there were two variants of the great novel begun in February 1850 and completed in August 1851; in the first draft, Ahab didn't exist, and the white whale was only incidental – a thesis Olson supports with reference to Melville's reading, specifically Melville's first reading of Shakespeare's *King Lear*. This was not a limited occurrence, as Olson has it, since Melville's reading long supported his writing, and it wasn't just Shakespeare:

> Melville's reading is a gauge of him, at all points of his life. He was a skald, and knew how to appropriate the work of others. He read to write. Highborn stealth, Edward Dahlberg calls originality, the act of a cutpurse Autolycus who makes his thefts as invisible as possible. Melville's books batten on other men's books.

Since Olson, much has been done to unearth Melville's reading matter, especially those books which were part of his own well-collected library (most of which was sold on after his death). One of the aims of my book of poems, *Of Whales: in Print, in Paint, in Sea, in Stars, in Coin, in House, in Margins* (Salt, 2010), was to take Melville's source materials to new ends, without leaving the whale or Melville behind. Some of the following poems (as well as the poem on page 57 of this book), then, feature epigraphs from various books Melville read during his composition of *Moby-Dick*. Some cite the very same passages Melville himself 'marginalised' with an *x* or an *o*, a checkmark, or a short annotated phrase. Other poems take Melville's novel, life or letters, or modern Melville scholarship as their springboard, incorporating lines or anecdote. Always, my will was to dive deep and beyond Melville's original. In this way, I hope to extend Melville's own tradition of reading to write, highborn stealth, the creation of a new book which is firmly battened on the books of others.

Mocha Dick

"We shall leave our adventurer to tell his own story, although not
always in his own words ..."

J. N. Reynolds, 'Mocha Dick: or, The White Whale of the Pacific:
a Leaf from a Manuscript Journal', 1839.

You could be my first mate, or I could be yours –
tracking the whiteness along the horizon
with an iron held high above my head.

I could be your loquacious sealer, or you could be mine,
lost in public for getting teary over the heart-stirring
harmony of a rookery just off the coast of this evergreen

and entirely deserted isle of Mocha.
We spend months learning the ropes of sublunary pursuits,
all the while knowing that only one of us will compel the other

with his tale. I'm banging my head
against the musical portion of the cabin furniture
when I spot the white whale first ...

and all I hold dear about our friendship is gone.
From time to time you quake, under the herk and jerk
of line spinning through the chocks ...

and I wake: not so good natured nor so sensible
but with the words to bring all hands to deck,
and all decks to hand – the first outbreak

of my selfishness since we left land.

Subwhale. 2009. Wax, hair.

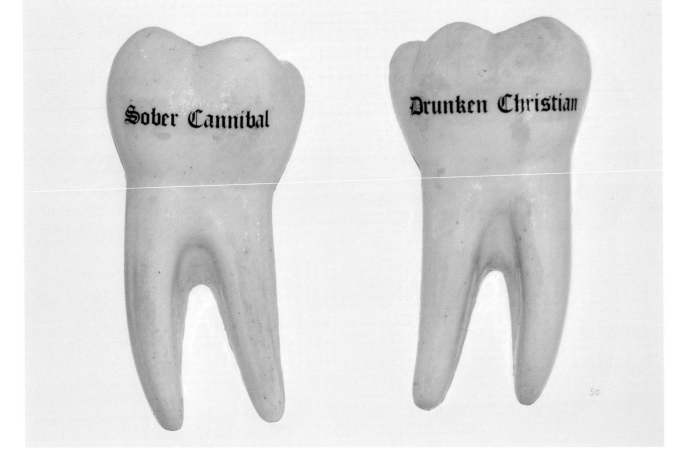

How I Met Your Mother (with the Help of Melville's)

"Rocborn advertises asparagus roots remarkably fine … I would advise
you to purchase five bundles at least."

Maria Gansevoort Melville in a letter to Anthony Caleshu, March 1851.

It's the first night in a week of nights that we haven't any
      Herman between us.
Not even a letter to his mother.

But now I'm remembering his mother's letters to him,
and to me, to whom she was always good to write.

Asparagus – she once told me – *roots*. It was a tip
in a time when a tip

of asparagus could get you killed. For months I piled the mounds
high, hiding the budding shoots

under the dirt which stained
the pretty skirt of the pretty girl

harvesting in the row next.
For adventure, some sons went to sea,

while some snapped
spears: whiter –

as I told Herman then
and I tell you now –

than any waves
or any whales.

A Plea on Behalf of the Sabbath for Whalemen

"Whaling captains and owners are seldom willing, for the honor of God
or regard to his law, to forego the profits … Oil got on the Sabbath
burns as well, sells as well, and, they think, spends as well as oil got
lawfully on weekdays."   *Rev. Henry T. Cheever, The Whale and His Captors, 1850.*

While I am off the coast of Goa, you are in Malaga.
While you are in Greenland, I am in the Netherlands,
learning the trade of the Biscayan and Dutch Whalemen.

For those years you are in the Seminaries of Andover
studying Tahitian theology for eventual deployment
to the tropical island of Rimatara, I sail, having

forgotten your freckled face, your fervent voice. It is not until
the third Sunday of my fourth month, mid-year, mid-century,
O how close you and I come to meeting …!

Just off the coast of Honolulu, Oahu while I am cutting in,
one of the lips, both me and it, covered with barnacles and
            Brobdignag lice.
I imagine the sight from shore: of gonies and haglets, the petrels
            and stinkards,

albatross and horse-birds, circling the ship. It's enough to stop
you from delivering your sermon: 'Zest after Rest: The Sabbath-
Keeping Experiences of the Very Reverend, Captain Scoresby,

and the Sufferings of Captain Hosmer and Boat's Crew of the
            Bark Janet.'
Before we ship out, I glimpse you just in time to wave goodbye …
but it's not until New Plymouth, New Zealand that I receive
            your plea:

Our contrasted lives of lights and shadows, of men damned and overboard,
of Sundays forgotten and forlorn. Sundry common excuses
you provide me with for my life's necessary defense.

I accept them greedily, offering not even this tribute in return.

The Chase and Capture

"There is a way to disclose paternity, declare yourself the rival of earth,
air, fire and water."
                                                    Charles Olson, Call Me Ishmael, 1947.

Our boat was like no other boat. We'd carved it
whole from Pacific coast Sequoia and manned it

with no headsman. Even though I had no stomach for it,
I'd employed us in the chase and capture,

packing three harpoons in a crate containing
a lantern, tinder-box, and other small articles of light.

When night came, we agonized over our bonds
to those we'd named

(Timor Jack, New Zealand Tom, Moby Dick),
just as we agonised over our bonds to each other.

The breaching came just as I was about
to disclose to you the true meaning of our outing.

When we abandoned our boat (stoved and taking on water)
I declared myself the rival of earth and air,

fire and water. We'd come to a land
once of cannibals, now of sons and daughters,

mothers and fathers. Just how we fit in
we're spending the rest of our lives to assay.

[ABOVE] *Leviathan Melvillei*. 2011. Plaster 36cm.
[RIGHT] Lace Teeth from *Jawstock*. 2011.

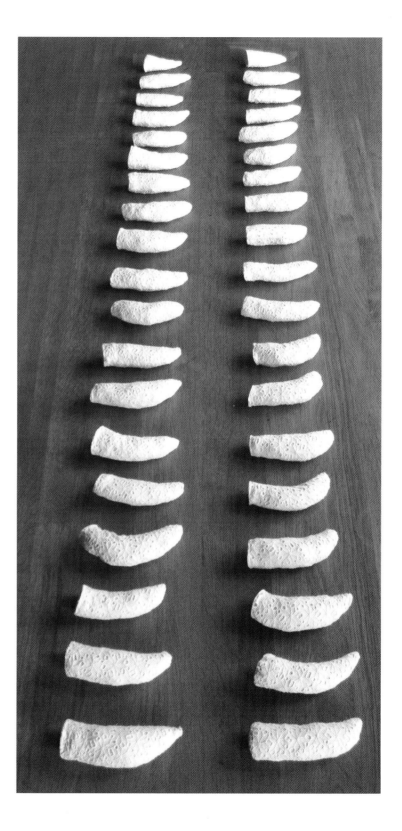

Chapter 66. 2007. Plaster, wax and lipstick.

No Whales Were Harmed in Making This House

"I built a cottage for Susan and myself, and made a gateway in the form
of a Gothic arch, by setting up a whale's jaw bones."

Nathaniel Hawthorne, Twice-Told Tales, 'The Village Uncle'.
Checked and marked in the margins by Herman Melville.

Our fellow villagers have avoided us ever since the beaching
became a beheading. Not everyone was ever going to help,

but having been to Hull and Homer, we felt the most expert
of the locals and organised the work – 24 hours to butcher

and a month to clean by exposure: weather and wolves,
then an alkaline soup to finish the job, eucalyptus and wheat grass,

dandelion stem and beetroot. We siphoned the remaining broth
onto the sweetgrass in the surrounding dunes,

from where we now get the silver and blue flowers we call
      whale's tails.
Bones were missing of course – vertebrae and ribs –

and so we carved and textured a local clay until even you
would be hard pressed to identify the fabricated from the originals.

The pointed tooth we each wear around our necks is real,
a double cone, and no doubt accounts for our newfound

liking of squid. *Man alone breathes by his mouth*,
so we've been told, and we laugh at those who think

we have any plans to do differently. The school children,
so far, are the only ones who stand below our cottage waiting.

We invite you, too, to experience the quietude of one
with no external ear. We've built a house out of bone

but know it's the articulation of suspension, the floating
we inhabit so high in the village sky, which causes the most distress.

[ABOVE] *Yankee*. 2009. Pewter and cornhusk found on shoreline.
[RIGHT] *12 Fishy Men*. 2010. Carved ribs (after the whale ship Essex)

Four pewter whales. 2010.

The Only Begat Poem in a Book of Begat Poems

"And his brother's name was Jubal:
he was the father of all such as handle
the harp and organ."

The Bible, 'Genesis', 4:21, (1845).
Triple marked by Melville in the right margin.

And Anthony begat Peter who begat Anthony Peter
whose brother was Peter and whose uncle was Peter
who was an excellent plumber and who had a regulation-
sized pool table in his house which overlooked the house
of his brother Bobby who had a swimming pool and
who sold hot-dogs and who made hot-dogs for all of the kids
swimming in the pool including his son Bobby
who would move to Florida where he would live
a couple of hours drive from his uncle Peter
who is my father who is your grandfather
who before he retired made fluorescent light bulbs
and who you are named after though your name is not Peter
just as mine is not Irad who begat Mehujael who begat
Methusael who begat Lamech who with Adah (meaning assembly)
begat Jabal and Jubal: meaning, respectively, *he that has cattle*
(as in, Where did you get the cattle?) and *trumpet*
(as in: Since your name is not Jubal, I think it's time
you put down that trumpet).

Recovered

"Most of Melville's marginal marks had been erased from his copy of [Thomas Beale's 'The Natural History of the Sperm Whale'], but all of the markings and much of his annotation are now recovered."

Steven Olsen-Smith, 'Introduction to Melville's Marginalia'.

We recover Melville's copy of Beale's *Natural History of the*
      Sperm Whale
floating in the South Pacific. Bloated and rebacked, abraded
      and die-stamped,

the dark green publisher's cloth and matching slipcase has
      been weathered
to an old whale's pale blue. In the past, our wish to read the
      marginal marks

would have left us as far from the truth as we are now from the land.
But after so many days of grey skies and rain we claim the
      advances of

digital technology, infrared lighting, x-ray glasses we squint
      through …
until … out of nothing, Melville's original pencil indentations

surface in the margins: single checks and double checks,
      various tickings
and tackings (Xs and Os) … And occasionally, so occasionally,

a pencil drawing of a right hand pointing me, I'm happy to say,
in the direction of you … and you – after two bad nights –

in the direction of the poor nurse of me.

Night Watch

"The eye is upon the whole small for the size of the whale ... Animals
that swim are in this respect similar to those that fly."

Thomas Beale, The Natural History of the Sperm Whale.
Triple checked and cross-marked by Melville.

If there is a place I fear losing you most
it is here:

in the extended blink of an eye.
Under my direction,

the boat's stern becomes its cutwater,
and under yours

no harpoon is thrown.
There is nothing voluntary

in your making it through
another night.

When I cradle your head, I count
the bones in your neck.

We've long suspected those that swim
related to those that fly. We contemplate

the whale's eye ... too small for his size.
When you close your eyes, I don't close mine.

Still Song

There comes a night when you don't want to read *Moby-Dick*
      anymore.

We have been floating on the margins of context for too long.

There is the rumour of squid big as our house, and jellyfish bright as
      this lamp

to contend with. The possibility that so much can (and will)

render our impressions meaningless

means all we can do is stomach on. All of the living

that has gone into our reading has informed our midnight walks:

we know only too well that there are no roses, no violets,
      no perfume at sea.

We comfort ourselves with the myth of morning

before returning thoughts of whales to depths

under our heads and under our pillows. Each sentence is a sentence

lost and found. Each word we say is a loud reminder

that for some time to come, we'll be seeking each other's approval.

We remind ourselves that it is just a book: even if it tells the story
      of our lives.

Pulpit. 2011. Plaster, dog bones, rope and bronze.

Fluke Board. 2010. Oak barrell top, pewter, dogfish darts.

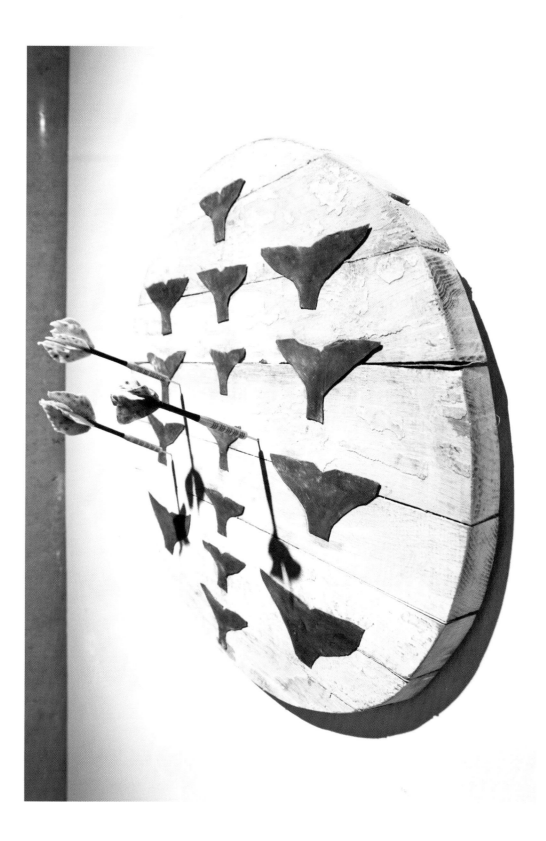

Stephen Grimes storyboards and images from set of John Huston's *Moby-Dick*. 1956.

CALL ME ISHMAEL
Philip Hoare on Stephen Grimes' designs for John Huston's
Moby-Dick, 1956

Reprinted from *Call Me Ishmael:*
An Exhibition on the theme of Moby-Dick,
Parfitt Gallery, Croydon, 28 February
– 8 April 2011.

In a strange and eerily silent sequence of scenes, their typed and epigrammatic directions like laconic intertitles, we witness the virtual recreation of a vast conceit. It's as if John Huston's film had only been imagined; as if Herman Melville's book might have been a dream. And for all their mid-century setting, there's something ancient, if not pagan, about these images. We see teeth impaled on bulwarks, men in belted overcoats. Sedate sea scenes, as if animated by a court artist, vie with bodies defying gravity and God as they fly into the air. All is mayhem and monstrosity, invested with the time-shifting power of imagination. The story is told, yet withheld.

It was hardly an innocent idea to begin with. 'I have written a blasphemous book', Melville boasted, 'and I feel as spotless as the lamb'. Stealing books from the New York Society Library, scribbling in their margins, he cut and pasted chunks like a nineteenth-century search engine, accruing evidence, embroidering his own experience. In one hallucinatory chapter, 'A Bower In The Arsacides', *Moby-Dick*'s unreliable narrator Ishmael seeks to have the measurements of the fantastical island whale temple, its bones gothically entwined with vines, tattooed on his arm. Melville too seemed to have the monstrous images of whales tattooed on his skin, embedded in his overgrown imagination. He was both Ishmael and Ahab, but he was also the great White Whale. If *Moby-Dick* is a book made mythic by the whale, the reverse is also true: Melville made a myth of the whale.

He never recovered from *Moby-Dick*. It was as if he didn't known what he'd written, and so required no-one's forgiveness. He had worked alone, in the upper room of his landlocked farmhouse in western Massachusetts, surrounded by harpoons and Polynesian weapons and blue-and-white china, peering out of his window at the snow-covered brow of Mount Greylock that reared up like a whale out of the countryside. Like *Wuthering Heights*, *Moby-Dick* appeared without precedent in the middle of the industrial century, the product of a person possessed. How could Melville wonder at its failure? Or doubt that a firestorm should sweep through the Manhattan warehouse of his publishers, destroying all remaining copies, as if history itself were determined that such blasphemy should not go unpunished?

It took a generation after Melville's death in 1891 before anyone realised what latent power lay in his book, squeezed between its boards like a whale in a stately home. *Moby-Dick* breached in a modern age. D. H. Lawrence called it a futurist text before futurism. It was an avatar of apocalyptic intent, ripe for reinvention. And so in 1953, as nuclear devices were exploding in the same South Seas in which the White Whale had swum a century before, John Huston embarked on his own version of *Moby-Dick*. It was a Herculean task.

Huston had the *Hispanola* – the same vessel used in Disney's film of *Treasure Island* – sailed to Hull, where, in the former Yorkshire whaling port, ancient chandlers' lofts were raided for original equipment to refit the ship. Tricked out as a cannibal craft, this reborn *Pequod* travelled to the west coast of Ireland to take up its role in Huston's film to a script by Ray Bradbury. By all accounts, as much action happened behind the camera as in front of it. One life-sized whale model escaped and had to be pursued by the RAF for fear it would pose a danger to shipping – a mimetic Moby Dick wreaking his vengeance anew. And during the filming of the final scene, Gregory Peck was strapped to the whale's flanks and dunked for take after take at the director's orders, nearly meeting the fate of the fictional character he was playing.

But the scenes that most astound me now – having first seen this film as a boy, on a tiny black and white television in suburban Southampton, unaware of the artfulness of a movie shot in both monochrome and Technicolor, the two prints combined to recreate the look of nineteenth-century seascapes – are the authentic whaling scenes shot by Huston's second unit in the island of Madeira. In the ultimate blurring of reality and art, Huston, in an Ahabian gesture, set out to kill his own whales. Tricked by cinematic editing into complicity, we watch as the island hunters of the *Santo Espirito* – an unholy spirit indeed – harpoon living whales in what is effectively a cetacean snuff movie. It was, after all, a new mid-century of destruction.

In the year that Huston made his film, more whales died around the world than were hunted in a century and a half of Yankee whaling. An age that had honed its human murder applied its efficiency to other species. Ishmael and his fellow whalers had been restricted in their crusade by a medieval armoury of harpoons and lances, the results cut up and rendered in alchemical tryworks that turned blubber into black gold. But now grenade harpoons and electric probes were clinically employed to cull whales for their impertinence, for idly boasting of being the largest, loudest, longest-lived animals. We punished their watery hubris from our airy arrogance.

And they died in their tens, their hundreds, their thousands. Sperm whales and right whales, fin whales and minkes, bowheads, Bryde's and blues, bodies bobbing in the Southern Ocean, ripped open so that the icy sea against which they had been protected in life could prevent them from burning their own bones in death. Their products tanned leather, strung tennis racquets, laced shoes, fed cats and dogs and humans and roses, made up make-up and won wars; nitro-glycerine was manufactured from whales, processing placid animals into instruments of war.

For centuries man – and they were generally men who inured themselves to their brutal, heroic, testosterone-fuelled actions – had represented whales as horned, roaring, spouting monsters at the edge of the world, or as nothing more than overgrown fish. Art was complicit in this deception, but the animals' own elusiveness hardly worked in their favour. They may be the biggest creatures in the world, but who could say they'd ever seen one? Even those who claim to have done so, like myself, can attest only to a composite, portmanteau animal, a glimpse of a dorsal or a fluke or a rostrum, or even something as airy as its blow – not water at all, but condensed gas. Hidden by the ocean's cloak, they might as well have never existed.

Such tantalising components merely made whales easier to destroy. They still do. These unseen animals die invisibly, through our despoliation of the ocean, through euphemistic 'bycatch', through the noise we pump into their environment, by all these subtle ways we have evolved of creating collateral destruction. By failing to sit for its portrait, the whale fatally failed to present its ID. A century and a half ago, Ishmael delivered his warning, one which went unheeded.

For all these reasons, then, any way you may look at it, you must needs conclude that the great Leviathan is that one creature in the world which will remain

unpainted to the last … The only mode in which you can derive even a tolerable idea of his living contour, is by going a whaling yourself; but by so doing, you run no small risk of being eternally stove and sunk by him. Wherefore, it seems to me you had best not be too fastidious in your curiosity touching this Leviathan.

And all this was accomplished in silence; ironic, given that whales live in a world of sound. If their victims had been able to scream, said the British hunters of the 1960s, their duties would have been unendurable. Then, in 1970, Roger Payne and Scott McVay released the song of the humpback whale. Suddenly, the dumb were given a voice. The haunting threnody, a looping, continually renewed cycle of sound, became a lament for our own guilt. If Moby Dick stove in the *Pequod*, his new age incarnation attempted a more spiritual provocation. Even now, the Voyager space probe is loaded with humpback song to greet aliens; while its moving parts, like those of the Hubble telescope, are lubricated with spermaceti oil, since it does not freeze in space. Meanwhile, nuclear submarines adopted the shape and sound of the whale in a further indictment of the human ability to turn beauty into violence.

In the space of a generation, for a generation launching into space, humanity lurched from hunting to watching, from regarding the whale as a resource to seeing it as a natural wonder; an emblem of the blue planet which we had seen for the first time from outer space. This sudden psychic switch triggered profound reverberations, like the whales' subsonic calls. We are in the middle of the story, rather than at its end. Progress does not apply. Whale science is barely thirty years old, about as old as the fragile moratorium on the hunting of great whales. Is there is a greater drama played out between human and natural history? How could such an animal fail to be a potent muse, freighted with all our insecurities and prejudices, our delusions and our hopes?

Perhaps we'd best be not too fastidious in our curiosity touching this Leviathan, for fear of what we find out. The sperm whale, the greatest of all predators, the original Moby Dick, also possesses the biggest brain. One day we may be able to interpret the sonic clicks with which it communicates with its own kind. But I'm not sure I want to know what it has been saying about us.

With one last shuddering roar and a great convulsion, trembling and threshing, the WHALE knocks the BOAT over, and

the men are thrown out, oars are tossed like kindling, the boat is swamped with water.

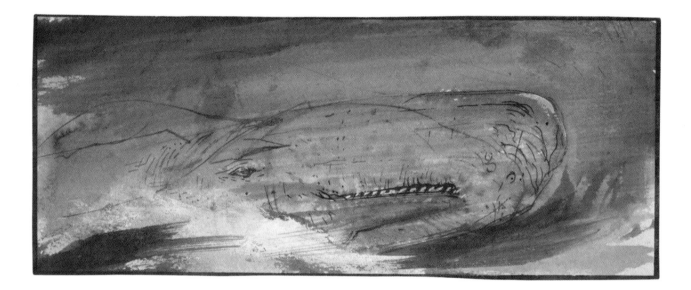

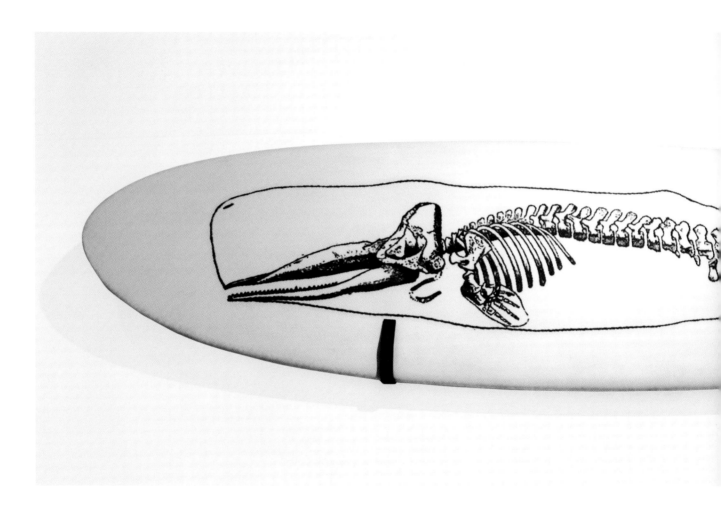

Whale board. 2011. From the film *Rachel's Orphan.*

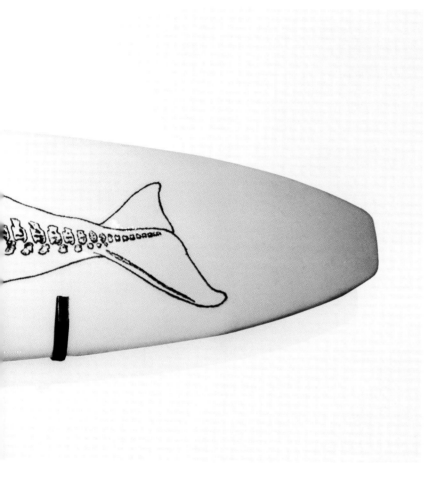

Hal Whitehead
Philip Hoare

THE CULTURAL LIFE OF WHALES
Philip Hoare in conversation with Hal Whitehead

Philip Hoare We're here today to talk about our two disciplines, which meet on a very specific subject, the whale. There are those who are working with this animal from a scientific point of view and those who are working with the whale from an artistic or literary point of view. What fascinates me is that that no matter what we do the whale always remains elusive.

For us as writers and artists, it is elusive because it is beyond description. I quickly ran out of superlatives talking about whales when I was writing my book *Leviathan or, The Whale*. But for you as a scientist it is elusive in that it is very difficult for you to study in the environment in which it lives. How did you come to the sperm whale specifically and what first draw you to it as a subject of study?

Hal Whitehead I think for most scientists the bigger mysteries are the more attractive ones. It's much more exciting to go for something which we really don't know. I think of all animals, the sperm whale is the one with the greatest mystery and possibility, and that I find very attractive. And I am assuming that this is what attracts writers and artists to the same animal.

PH That's precisely right. For me there is a degree of romance about the subject. Writing about whales has brought me into close contact with scientists and given me a new understanding about the animal. Your book *Sperm Whales: Social Evolution in the Ocean* talks specifically about sperm whale culture, but what do you mean by 'culture' when you apply it to this animal?

HW When a biologist like myself starts talking about culture they raise eyebrows from scholars in other disciplines who see themselves as the 'knowers' of culture. But, for a biologist, culture is primarily a flow of information – both ideas and behaviours – between the animals of a population, which they do by learning from each other.

This is interesting for biologists as the flow of information is what biology is about. Without information getting from one animal or plant to another, there would be no life. We as biologists have concentrated on genes as the way information gets through, but there are other ways in which this can happen – of which culture is one of them.

Culture leads to a whole new range of processes for animals, such as sperm whales, which don't happen in most animals or plants. Culture is what artists do, and it is what scientists do. The possibility that other groups of animals, which have these two flows of information through their population, they are interacting in extraordinary ways, leads, I think, to the idea that we have a creature of great mystery and great potential. This is what fundamentally intrigues me about culture and the whales. With the sperm whales, we biologists went into what we were doing by trying to explain what we found by using the principals of genetic evolution. But we started finding things that we couldn't explain satisfactorily, so we had to bring in other things. The process that made sense for these genetically unexplainable features was culture.

For example, I was studying a group of whales off the Galápagos Islands, looking at their social systems, and found two kinds of sperm whales who were behaving really quite differently, they had different ways of communicating with each other, different ways of using the resources around the island, etc. So the initial explanation was that we had two sub-species. But when we looked, there was virtually no difference genetically. So something else was causing these sperm whales to form two radically different societies, with radically different ways of behaving. It became obvious that the only explanation was that these whales had different cultures. They were living in a multicultural society.

PH Sperm whales communicate pre-eminently via the click system – the series of low sounds that they create within their heads – their individual sonar devices. But how far is the communication an expression of their culture?

HW There are ethnic markers in each sperm whale's vocal message which signify its cultural grouping. This is a very interesting feature because it is has been suggested by anthropologists that this is one of the key features of human culture. We don't know for sure, but we have strong indications of this.

PH Recently, there was a report on the notion of non-human intelligence in other species which placed dolphins above primates and behind humans. I wonder, given that the sperm whale has such a big brain and such a highly developed neocortex, how far do you think we are talking about animals which are quite close to human beings in their culture, in their social organisations, in the way in which they use their brains? How can we find out how whales use their brains?

HW It is something incredibly difficult to get a handle on. There have been a number of studies on various cognitive tasks on dolphins, but all these tests have been designed by humans, based on how we see our world, how we interact with it. Dolphins and sperm whales live in a completely different world, which is structured very differently to ours, where different things are very important.

Whales, largely, sense and communicate acoustically, whereas we do nearly all of our sensing visually. They live in a three-dimensional world; we live in a two-dimensional world. We are trying to relate them to what we are in metrics which correspond to how we see the world. But the other side of this is that the potential mysteries are even greater. I think it very likely that whales are doing things which, at the moment, we can't even conceive of – we are not operating in that world. So this is a real challenge for scientists to look for things that you don't know what you are looking for.

I want to try and move into this area and this is where people like you come in because artists, writers, and so on aren't constrained by the scientific process as it has grown up. You can speculate, think, try and put yourself in the world of the whale. And then, I think it possible that open-minded scientists, by looking at some of the products which artists produce, we may end up with hypotheses and ideas that will lead our research into ways that will crack this great mystery.

Another idea, which came from a discussion with a writer, Jeff Warren, is to use a virtual world as close as we can get to the real world of the whale to explore some of the ideas of what it might mean to be a whale. People go into this virtual world and live in it and through their changing experiences we can get some idea of what it is to be a whale.

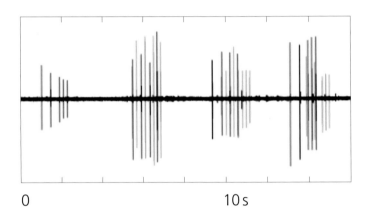

0   10 s

Coda exchange between two sperm whales. This plots sound pressure against time.
Each vertical line is a click. At intervals of 2-3 seconds there are:

1. "1+1+3" [click-pause-click-pause-click-click-click] coda made by one whale
2. "4R" [four regularly-spaced clicks] coda by one whale overlapping with a "4R" by the other
3. "4R" overlapping with "1+1+3"
4. "1+1+3" overlapping with "1+1+3"

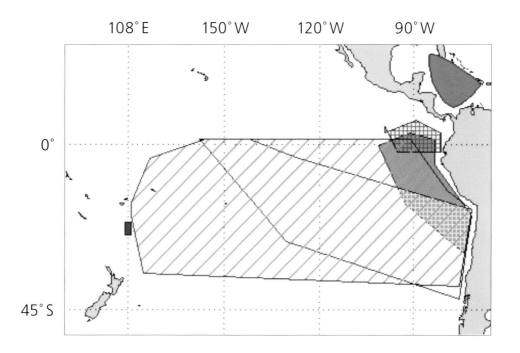

Sperm whale clans in the South Pacific

PH There things we need to do with our brain, pay the mortgage, drive a car, write a book, etc., that a whale obviously doesn't have to do and, as you say, the whale lives in an element in which we cannot live.

Unlike us, the whale lives in a three-dimensional environment which covers seventy per cent of the world's surface. How far do you think the whale is using its brain as a reflection of the vastness of its environment? Would it need a big brain to compute that environment?

HW Potentially. Because whales live in this very large three-dimensional habitat and they don't have a physical structure which is home for them, they are always on the move. The most important part of the environment for the whale is each other and social life is vital.

As they move around, everything is changing except their social lives. To me, it seems very likely that for these animals social life is even more important than it is for terrestrial animals, including humans. Relatively it has a much bigger role in their world. Therefore dealing with their social lives is absolutely vital – there needs to be intelligence about it.

Whales are a cultural species and not only it is important to maintain and nourish the social relationships which they depend on, but also to make really good use of the information which is flowing amongst these social partners. My guess is that those have been the drivers of the big and complex brain rather more than the direct need to keep track of a large and complicated environment.

PH That is really interesting as it raises the notion that for a whale, culture is more important than it might be for a human. In a way, it also raises the notion that the way whales use their brains, and the way culture is essential to their well-being, is an invisible process.

Could you describe the technical way the sperm whale communicates? I read that when sperm whales gather, they bring their heads together and there might be some way in which this intensifies the communication process, is this true?

HW Whales probably communicate in a lot of ways. The ones we know about are the ones that are most obvious to us, but this doesn't mean that they are necessarily the ones which are most important to sperm whales; they are just the ones which we have a means of getting our heads around. At short range, whales are vey tactile animals. They spend a lot of time in contact with each other and communicate through touch and this, presumably, is really important.

Unlike us, whales don't have obvious ways to change their bodies as a method of communication, such as our facial expressions, so vision for whales probably isn't so important. However, I suspect whales have a very detailed view of the outline of each other's bodies and this almost certainly conveys information between whales, perhaps involuntarily.

The sounds they make also appear to be communicative. Sperm whales do this in a strange way – about a quarter of their bodies are these huge sonar systems which make very large clicks and which allow them to find food deep under the ocean. But they use the same system to communicate with each other. The whales take these clicks and modify them and put them into patterns. I, and others, have tried to figure out what these patterns mean – one thing is clear, that these patterns appear to be used as means of reinforcing bonds. So you see individuals making duets of clicks, responding to each other, repeating patterns. It is likely that these patterns are part of the toolset they use to maintain their vital social relationships.

PH What fascinates me is the notion that these animals, like us, might start to rationalise their place in the world. What they mean, what their existence means. This is something you have hypothesised upon. I am not asking you to tell me what a whale might be thinking about, but do you think it is possible that a whale can have an existential sense of itself?

HW It is conceivable and it is one of the mysteries that attract me to this area. By living in a situation where social relationships and culture is very important, things like the serious mind having a concept of what others know, and therefore a concept of self, become more likely. In turn, this would obviously lead to one contemplating the self in the environment and how that fits together.

As whales are cultural species, ideas are being passed between individuals and down through generations which relate to this. I am not sure how we get to prove this yet but the possibility is certainly out there!

PH When I read about your hypothesis that whales have developed their own religion and that they have a sense of morality because of the way they interact which each other, I couldn't believe it. I think I am right in saying that their sonar, with which they communicate, is also used to hunt – I saw it myself in New Zealand when I watched a sperm whale use its sonar to stun kingfish at the surface to eat. But the notion that these animals have the power to cause damage to one another, which is where they might develop as a social complex a sense of morality. Is this right?

HW Sperm whales have the most powerful sonar in the natural world. It is very directional and extremely powerful. To use the sonar effectively, you not only need to make a click, you need to hear it. Any ear damage would be very dangerous, as some people have said; a deaf whale is a dead whale. Whales have got to look after their ears. Therefore it seems highly likely that if a sperm whale's sonar system was directed at another whale's ears, it would be very dangerous for the receiver. Whales are social animals – imagine about a group of twenty to thirty sperm whales feeding at depth, each making these dangerous clicks about once a second. They are all in the same area as each other so they need to be really careful. To me it is like having a bunch of hunters with machine guns out in the forest, they are firing away pretty continuously and they have got to have pretty clear rules about how they are going to do this if they are all going to come out of the forest routinely. I think there must be some conventions which are abided by about how you use these sonar systems. This, by some definitions at least, is morality.

PH This is very interesting from the point of view of what we are doing with the University of Plymouth. We are staging a symposium and exhibition about the whale, of which you will be a part, trying to bring together those who think about whales from the point of view of art or literature and those who work hands on – as it were – with whales. You said earlier that you thought it quite helpful for scientists to look at whales from an artist's perspective. For me as a writer, the big problem is anthropomorphism – to write about animals from a human perspective it is difficult to not be anthropomorphic as it is, really, the only way we humans can describe them. The whale, and especially the sperm whale, invites that because we know so little and because the science around these animals is so recent, only about three decades old.

Could you project, perhaps into a hundred years' time, where we might reach with whale science? How would you want science to move forward and what tools to do you need?

HW Whale science has been very tool dominated – unlike the study of apes, but then they are much closer both in terms of evolution and habitat. This has advantages, as we have been able to find out things we couldn't have without these nice devices, but it also means that we sometimes get sidetracked thinking about the technicalities, rather than the animals.

One thing that is clearly happening is that sophisticated tags which can be put on whales for short periods of time can give very detailed perspective on the behaviour of the animals. For instance, ten years ago we had almost no idea how a sperm whale feeds at depth but because of these tags, amongst other things, we are getting quite a good idea.

We are also getting much better very quickly and will know much more about the life of the whale in the future. To me, it will be very interesting when these techniques are brought to bear on the social end of things – the role of culture, the role of the brain in whales; this is where the puzzle is biggest and hardest.

It is possible that we use the same devices to learn about this – by measuring heart rates we can see how heart rates change as different things happen to the animals socially, when they meet a friend, hear an unfamiliar pattern of clicks. We can look at how they interact with each other physically – how does the hearing of the clicks change their movements in subtle ways?

Then, using other techniques, this can hopefully be related to individuals. As we build up on histories of individuals we can see how they vary and how these differences affect society – personalities and so on. I see this as the way forward.

But I am likely to be wrong and there could be an idea developed, perhaps by an artist, that figures out a way to show some new dimensions of the whale. The culture and brain of the whale is a vast mystery and something really hard to get at scientifically.

PH We are talking about human culture meeting whale culture. That's necessarily what I try to do when I write about whales, but it is what you physically do by being in the field with whales. And there is the aspect of the way in which our culture affects whales – historically through hunting and now through the way we are changing the planet, through climate change, through pollution. For instance, when I was in Maine recently, I learned from Dr John Wise there that sperm whales, because they inhale so deeply, may be breathing in heavy metals in the air.

The great dilemma is, are we changing whales by observing them? Whale watching raises the animal's profile but are we influencing its behaviour? In the future, will that meeting of cultures be in any way reciprocal? Can we reach such a point where we understand the whales' communications and they can communicate to us? A dog communicates to you – a sperm whale is way more intelligent – so do you think interspecies communication is possible?

HW That's a tough one! We try to leave minimal impact in our research as we are trying to find out what whales do naturally. But some of the more profound and interesting things we know about whales have come of animals in captivity and this of course is getting more and more problematic as captivity is a very unreal environment to the whale.

However, how do we go on if we don't want to keep whales in captivity but all our methods for learning about their cognition and communication are developed for captive animals? Lori Marino and Toni Frohoff have proposed that we try to take these techniques into the wild using animals that seek out humans. This is controversial, but to me it is very challenging and if it can be shown to work we can learn about cognitive processes in whales by making use of those which naturally seek us out – it could be extremely productive as you have animals in their natural environment, in situations where you have enough control over what is happening to get a feel of what they are thinking, how they are making decisions.

[ABOVE] *Nomenclature or Anvil Fish*. 2010, Anvil, dried pet gold fish.
[RIGHT] *White balled*. 2009. Snooker balls.

Believe It Can Be Done. 2009. Gannet, magnum bottle, wax.

[ABOVE] *The Gam*. 2008. Wax crustacean claws hairgrips, bottle wires.
[RIGHT] *Shark Fin Cola*. 2009. Tope fins and coke bottle.

Thar She Blows. 2011. Megaphones.

SONGS OF THE WHALERMEN
Sam Richards

Blow Boys Blow
Tis advertised in Boston
New York and Buffalo
Five hundred young Americans
A-whaling for to go

And its blow ye winds of morning
Blow ye winds high-ho
Clear away your running gear
And blow boys blow

They take you down to Bedford
That famous whaling port
And give you to some landsharks
To board and fit you out

It's then that they will show you
Their whaling ships so stout
They say you'll have five hundred sperm
Before you're six months out

It's now we're out to sea my boys
The wind comes on to blow
One half the watch is sick on deck
The other half sick below

It's now up to the masthead
All of us must go
And when you see them sperm whales
You sing out 'There she blows'

Then clear away the boats my boys
And after him we'll travel
And if you get too near his flukes
He'll kick you to the devil

Now we've turned him upside down
We'll tow him alongside
And over with our blubber hooks
To rob him of his hide

And now we're bound for Tombas
That damned old whaling port
And if you run away my boys
You surely will be caught

Now we got home our ship made fast
We're finished with our sailing
A winding glass around we'll pass
And damn this blubber whaling

It wasn't that long ago when you could sing songs of the whaling trade quite unapologetically in concerts, folk clubs or on record and hope that everyone would join in the chorus. In fact, some of the early folksong revival's best-known recorded albums bore titles such as *Thar She Blows* or *Leviathan* – and were sung by radically left-wing singers such as A. L. Lloyd or Ewan MacColl – who, if they had been alive today, may well have been on the side of 'Save the Whale'.

In point of fact, and probably unknown to the world of the folk revival, negotiations to save the whale from extinction have been taking place since the International Convention for the Regulation of Whaling in 1948. It was this body that eventually, in 1986, outlawed all whaling in international waters, and at this time many countries made whaling illegal in their own waters. Since then a whole slew of other regulations have come about to protect endangered species. Illegal whaling does go on, although Greenpeace and others have committed themselves to combating it.

In view of all this it might be asked why we continue to celebrate the whaling trade through focussing on novels like Melville's *Moby-Dick*, or by showing the John Huston movie and, perhaps most of all, by singing the songs of the whalermen. And the answer, really, is the same as in other such cases. Do we stop staging Shakespeare's *Merchant of Venice* because it could feed anti-Semitism? Do we stop reading eighteenth and nineteenth-century classic novels because of the sexism inherent in the society they portray? Do we avoid Gauguin's paintings because we disapprove of his behaviour with young Tahitian maidens? We accept that all these examples are historical; therefore we don't necessarily express our support for everything about them merely because we read, watch or listen to them. Expressive culture exists in the context of its own times. And, of course, it has to be said that there are bound to be things we do which future generations will find uncomfortable.

In the case of sea songs – of all kinds (not just whaling songs) – many of them are so colourful, so extraordinarily dramatic, and tell their tales in such compellingly powerful ways, that we need little real excuse for singing them. Like so many ballads and songs of occupations, they were written from the *inside*, by insiders – either that or by songwriters very close to the inside. They had to be. Anything inauthentic, any wrong details, would simply not have been tolerated by those who knew these occupations inside out. And whaling was the most dramatic of all seafaring occupations – mainly because it was the most dangerous. Ordinary sailors on board merchantmen in the great days of sail certainly had their rough times, storms, their awful grub, bullying bosuns and cruel captains. But the whalermen had all that *plus* the combat with the whale, which could be fatal, as is illustrated by this next song – one of the best known whaling songs. It is usually simply called *The Greenland Whale Fishery*.

The Greenland Whale Fishery
In eighteen hundred and forty nine
On March the seventeenth day
We hoisted out colours to our topmast high
And for Greenland bore away brave boys
And for Greenland bore away

And when we reached that icy shore
With our gallant ship in full fold
We wished ourselves back safe at home again
With our friends all on the shore brave boys
With our friends all on the shore

Our captain stood on the fo'c'stle head
With a spyglass in his hand

There's a whale, there's a whale, there's a whalefish he cried
And she blows on every span brave boys
And she blows on every span

And when this whale we did harpoon
She gave a flurry with her tail
She capsized the boat and we lost five men
And we did not catch that whale brave boys
And we did not catch that whale

Now the losing of those five gallant men
It grieved our captain full sore
But the losing of that hundred barrel whale
Well it grieved him ten times more brave boys
It grieved him ten times more

Then hoist your anchor and away, cried he
Let us leave this cold country
Where the whalefishes blow and the stormy winds do blow
And the daylight's seldom seen brave boys
And the daylight's seldom seen

The songs and ballads of the whaling trade give perhaps the best possible introduction to the kinds of lives led by the rough, tough whalermen who mixed a robust sturdiness with a kind of superstitious religiosity, a violent trade with genuine artistic sensibility, as can be seen in scrimshaw – those exquisite engravings on the bones or teeth of sperm whales – or, indeed, in their songs.

In Melville's *Moby-Dick* there is one short chapter given over to an account of singing and music on board the *Pequod*. These few pages give an insight into context for singing these songs. The chapter is headed 'Midnight, Forecastle' and is only seven pages long, but its description provides some historical evidence for the vernacular song and musical culture of the whalermen.

One of the first things we notice in this chapter is how multicultural the crew was. You can count at least sixteen nationalities including – apart from American and English – French, Icelandic, Maltese, Dutch, Chinese, Tahitian, Manx, Spanish, Portuguese and many others. This melting pot perhaps reminds us of New Orleans at the turn of the twentieth century when jazz was born, or of the port of Liverpool at many times in its history – including the 1950s and 1960s when the Mersey scene that gave rise to The Beatles was stimulated by American imported records, a history of Irish migration, and the UK's most historically rooted black population. Quite possibly London today, with its many musical vernaculars from a range of ethnic backgrounds, offers a similar case. Culturally and expressively speaking, melting pots are creative.

We might expect this ethnic mix to be reflected in the songs of the whalers – and they undoubtedly were in real life. However, the only lines of song quoted by Melville are from very well-known British/American songs. One we have already encountered. *The Greenland Whale Fishery* contains some lines very close in wording to those sung by a character that Melville calls a Nantucket sailor who sings:

Our captain stood upon the deck
A spy-glass in his hand
A viewing of those gallant whales
That blew at every strand

Melville actually says that 'all follow' the song. However, it seems that the Nantucket sailor's verses are, as Melville gives them, a little mixed up, for *The Greenland Whale Fishery*, as he gives it, runs straight into these lines:

So, be cheery, my lads! May your hearts never fail!
While the bold harpooner is striking the whale

Now it is more than possible that some song existed with this as its chorus, but it doesn't appear in any of the standard collections. However, these lines do have the meter, the swing, and some of the words, of a whaling song called *The Bonny Ship the Diamond*, a Scots song celebrating the whaling crew and their girlfriends ashore in Peterhead.

The Bonnie Ship The Diamond
The Diamond is a ship, me lads, for the Davis Straight she's bound
And the quay it is all garnished with bonny lasses round
Captain Thomson gives the order to sail the ocean wide

When the sun it never sets my lads, nor darkness dims the sky

CHORUS
So it's cheer up my lads, let your hearts never fail
While the bonnie ship The Diamond goes a-fishing for the whale

Along the quay at Peterhead the lasses stand around
With their shawls all pulled about them and the salt tears running down
But don't you weep my bonnie lass, though you be left behind
For the rose will grow on Greenland's ice before we change our mind

Here's a health to the Resolution, likewise the Eliza Swan
Here's a health to the Battler of Montrose and The Diamond, ship of fame
We wear the trousers of the white and the jackets of the blue
When we return to Peterhead we'll have sweethearts enou'

It will be bright both day and night when the Greenland lads come home
With a ship that's full of oil, my lads, and money to our name
We'll make the cradle for to rock and the blankets for to tear
And every lass in Peterhead sing 'hushabye my dear'

There are various other notable details in Melville's midnight on the fo'c'stle scene. For example, when half a dozen sailors have a dance they do so to the music of the tambourine – and nothing else. The sailor from the Azores shouts: 'Go it, Pip! Bang it, bell-boy! Rig it, dig it, stig it, quig it, bell-boy! Make fire-flies; break the jinglers!'

The 'jinglers' are the jingles on the tambourine. And Pip does indeed 'break the jinglers'. As he says: 'there goes another, dropped off. I pound it so.' We can imagine how hard he did 'pound' the tambourine to make the jingles fly. However, Tashtego, one of the black sailors, is unimpressed. He says: 'That's a white man; he calls that fun: humph! I save my sweat.' One would dearly wish to know what Tashtego would have expended his sweat on, but Melville doesn't supply this detail.

The whole chapter opens with a kind of stage direction in brackets which reads:

(Foresail rises and discovers the watch standing, lounging, leaning, and lying in various attitudes, all singing in chorus.)

Now, the chorus they are singing – and Melville specifically gives these lines to 'Harpooneers and Sailors' (which presumably covers every labourer in the crew) – is none other than that fine old ballad *Spanish Ladies*. I say 'old' because it was old then – Melville's novel was first published in 1851 – and was well known to seafaring people. According to Captain Marryat's *Midshipman Easy*, published in the 1840s, however, this song was, by then, 'almost forgotten' – but this simply wasn't true, as various subsequent folksong collections show. Furthermore, a number of different trades produced their own version. For the whaling trade an anonymous lyricist produced a version in which the old chorus of 'We'll rant and we'll roar like true British sailors' was replaced by 'We'll rant and we'll roar like true born young whalermen'. The verses say little about the actual job of hunting and killing the sperm whales found around the coasts of Peru and Chile. Instead, they celebrate the girls of the Chilean town of Talcahuano, just south of Valparaiso – which was known to English-language sailors as 'Vallypo'. Tumbez, also mentioned in the whaler's version of the song, is on the Gulf of Guayquil, near the Equator. A. L. Lloyd, the singer and folklorist who spent a season or two on Antarctic whaling ships, called them 'odorous ports, all three'. Odorous or not, the girls of Talcahuano obviously had some appeal for the whalermen of the nineteenth century.

Talcahuano Girls
Now I've been a sea cook and I've been a clipperman
I can dance, I can sing, I can walk the jib-boom
I can handle a harpoon and cut a fine figure
Whenever I get in a boat's standing room

CHORUS
And we'll rant and we'll roar like true born young whalermen
We'll rant and we'll roar on deck and below
Until we see bottom inside the two sinkers
And straight up the channel to Huasca we'll go

I was in Talcahuano last year in a whaler
I bought some gold brooches for the girls in the Bay
I bought me a pip and they called it a meersh'm
And it melted like butter on a hot summer's day

I went to a dance one night in old Tumbez
There was plenty of girls there as fine as you'd wish
There was one pretty maiden a-chewing terbaccer
Just like a young kitten a-chewing fresh fish

Here's a health to the girls of old Talcahuano
A health to the maidens of far-off Maui
Let you be merry, don't be melancholy
I can't marry youse all or in chokey I'd be

There are songs, quite a big handful of them, that describe the actual combat with the whale. One of the best is *The Coast of Peru* – with some vivid, if gory, detail about the actual kill. One verse, for example, pretty well justifies the accusation of cruelty that gathered strength in the latter twentieth century:

He raced and he sounded, he twist and he spin
But we fought him alongside and got our lance in
Which caused him to vomit, and the blood for to spout
And in ten minutes time, my boys, he'd rolled both fins out

… which gives a clear idea of how brutal the whole thing was.

But it wasn't only brutal for the whales. The whalermen were an odd lot who could never guarantee coming home alive – if at all. Whales, quite simply, don't relish being harpooned and tend to fight to the death once attacked, as do all hunted animals. Once a whale had been sighted, usually with the cry of 'there she blows', the ship would put out small rowing boats with harpooners who, dare devils as they and the oarsmen were, would get as close as possible to the whale itself – close enough for the harpooners to throw their long spears. There are many accounts – as in *The Greenland Whale Fishery* – of boats being capsized and men being lost overboard. All this stopped in the 1880s with the use of the harpoon cannon, which meant that much bigger whales could be tackled, at greater (and safer) distances and speeds. It was this, in the end, which led to the over-fishing of whales and their endangerment. It was the era of the hand harpooners that produced all the whaling ballads and songs, incidentally.

What made a man sign up for this hazardous job? For some young men it was an escape from undesirable circumstances – perhaps a life in which nothing other than the predictable happened – a condition which might be cured by the tang of adventure. Melville's narrator, Ishmael, is of this variety. After the well-known opening sentence, 'Call me Ishmael', he goes on to say:

> Some years ago – never mind how long precisely – having little or no money in my purse, and nothing particular to interest me on shore, I thought I would sail about a little and see the watery part of the world.

These loners, these oddballs from seaport towns, roughnecks and adventurers were joined by some from the criminal classes. If you signed up and seemed tough enough there were very few captains who were in the least bit bothered about what you'd done previously. Good tough men were in demand in the whaling trade, no questions asked – men who knew that they'd be away for a long, long time. A. L. Lloyd told the story of a merchantman who met a whaling ship in the Indian Ocean.

> Her rigging was hung with weeds, her paint all gone, and bleared old men were lined along her rail. The merchantman hailed: 'How long from home?' Back came the hollow cry: 'We don't know. We was young men when we sailed.'

There may have been something to have been said for a life of virtual imprisonment for some months, only broken by hazardous adventures, Arctic or Antarctic conditions, storms and gales, followed by whoring and boozing on shore for brief periods. At least, this is the life the whalermen signed up for and frequently sang about. Typical are these two verses of *Rolling Down to Old Maui* – one of the Hawaiian islands that was known as a whaling port where ships were fitted out for voyages and where, inevitably, there were plenty of fleshly attractions. The ice, snow and polar seas make a harsh contrast to the warmth of the Hawaiian girls who laugh and chat and make you feel a lot better.

Rolling Down to Old Maui
It's an ample share of toil and care

We whalemen undergo
Through many a blow of frost and hail
The bitter squalls of snow
The horrid isles of ice-cut tiles
The deck the polar sea
But now we're bound from the Arctic ground
Rolling down to old Maui

Once more we're blown by the northern gale
And bounding o'er the main
And the green hills of them tropical isles
We soon shall see again
Oh, it's many a day we toiled away
In that cold Kamchatka Sea
And we'll think of that as we laugh and chat
With the girls of old Maui

There is a somewhat formulaic poetry in many of the whaling songs. Of all the destinations in the world Greenland is the most often mentioned, and it is always described as 'icy' or bleak in some other way. Some songs borrow from an unrelated ballad, *The Lowlands of Holland*, in describing Greenland as a 'dreadful place' in which there is 'no green' and 'the daylight's seldom seen'. A huge number of the songs mention sweethearts and wives left behind, often weeping. When the whalermen return they generally 'make the taverns roar' and the bed blankets tear. Typically, the parting shot often tells of how – when the break is over – they'll go back to sea for more.

Greenland Bound
Once more for Greenland we are bound
To leave you all behind
Our ship is painted green and our blubber hooks are keen
And we sail before the icy wind

We left our sweethearts and our wives
A-weeping on the pier
Cheer up my dear, we soon shall return
For it's only half a year

With tarry dress we reached Stromness

Where we did go ashore
With whalemen scarce and water even less
We had to take on more

And when we came to the Northern ice
We crowded on full sail
Each boat was manned with a keen and lively hand
All for to hunt the whale

Now dark and dreary grows the night
And the stars begin to shine
With the chasing of the whale and the trying of the oil
That it seems like we'll never return

Our six months being done, we tie up again
And the lads all go ashore
It's plenty of brass and a bonny bonny lass
For to make them taverns roar

To Greenland's frost we'll drink a toast
And to them we love so dear
And across the icy main to the whaling grounds again
We'll take a trip next year

Finally, there were the work songs, the shanties. These were not peculiar to the whaling trade. All merchantmen had a shanty singer. His craft was to holler out the lines while the crew heaved or hauled while singing the chorus line. Shantymen were one of the last examples of oral composition. Out of traditional fragments, scraps of verse and well-known references they composed (perhaps re-composed is the more accurate word) on the spot, often larding their lyrics with earthy sentiments. The one heard in the movie of *Moby-Dick*, where the singer, incidentally, is A. L. Lloyd who I've referred to a couple of times now, is *Blood Red Roses*.

I commented earlier on the multicultural mix on board ship, and it is well known that different ethnic groups influenced one another musically and verbally. In this respect I've always felt that there's something vaguely bluesy about *Blood Red Roses* to the extent that it would be very easy to imagine it as an African-American work song.

If you listen to field recordings of work songs from the Caribbean (the Bahamas, for example) you can begin to hear the meeting of black and white.

Blood Red Roses
Me boots and clothes is all in pawn
Go down, you blood red roses, Go down
And it's flamin' drafty 'round Cape Horn
Go down, you blood red roses, Go down
Oh, you pinks and posies
Go down, you blood red roses, Go down

But it's round Cape Horn we all must go
For that is where them whalefish blow

It's growl you may but go you must
If you growl too hard your head they'll bust

It's 'round that cape we all must go
Around all stiff through the frost and snow

It's when you're walloping round Cape Horn
You wish to Christ you'd never been born

When I was a young man in my prime
I could take them pretty girls nine at a time

But now I'm old and getting grey
I can only manage two a day

My old mother she wrote to me
My dearest son come home from sea

Just one my pull and that'll do
For we're the boys to pull her through

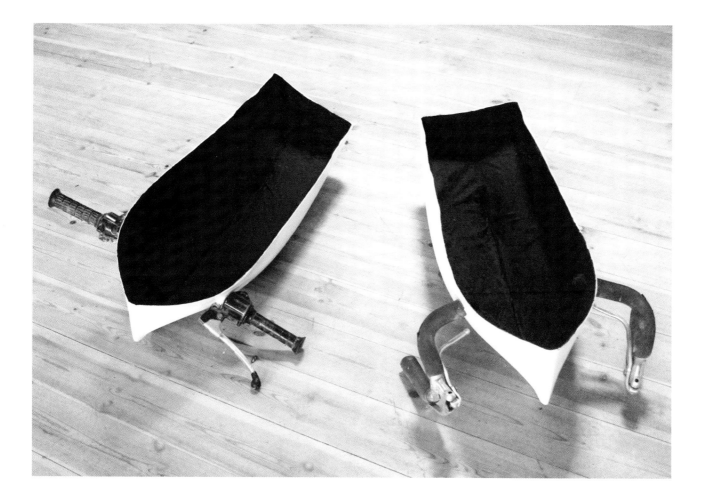

Nantucket Sleigh Ride. 2009. Fibre glass, damask and bike handles.

Truth and Reconciliation. 2011. From the film *Rachel's Orphan*.

BEGINNING'S ENDS
Michael Hall

London, 2011

On the second day, a sail drew near, nearer, and picked me up at last. It was the devious-cruising Rachel, that in her retracing search after her missing children, only found another orphan.[1]

This is the full stop that signals the end of the first Great American Novel, Herman Melville's *Moby-Dick*. It's a strangely romantic ending, steeped in melancholy, to a great tragedy. In a direct reference to the novel's conclusion, Angela Cockayne's filmed performance, *Rachel's Orphan*, signals the end of *Dominion*, a multi-faceted and multi-layered exploration of the social, political and experiential association to the whale – but not any whale: Melville's whale, Moby Dick.

And I only am escaped alone to tell thee.[2]

As we are led into the epilogue, Melville chooses to ignore an important fact. There are actually two survivors, the second being the albino sperm whale Moby Dick. The 'monster' from Melville's novel would become the recognisable picture of the whale, the face of the many, seeking vengeance for our obsessive abuse. The decimated whale that would fuel the Industrial Revolution, light homes and fuel wars, has become a creature that we can only feel a great sadness for when reflecting on its sacrifice for us. These Leviathans of the sea are creatures of such beauty and mystery that they have continued to occupy the dreams, thoughts and ideas of many a scientist, artist, writer and poet, both before *Moby-Dick* and for the 160 years since it was first published.

But, though the world scouts at us whale hunters, yet does it unwittingly pay us the profoundest homage; yea, an all-abounding adoration! For almost all the tapers, lamps, and candles that burn around the globe, burn, as before so many shrines, to our glory![3]

Working in collaboration with author Philip Hoare and composer Nick Atkinson, Angela Cockayne has spent the last four years developing the many layers of *Dominion*, a cut-and-paste job not dissimilar to that of Melville and a worthy shrine to his glory. *Dominion* manifests itself as a re-appropriation of Melville's many musings. With Cockayne's images and objects, Hoare's written words and the emotive compositions by Atkinson, the work is layered with an atmospheric beauty and contemplative self-awareness. If Thomas Beale's *The Natural History of the Sperm Whale* can be considered as the lost manuscript for *Moby-Dick*, then the many ambiguous responses to his novel in Dominion are a worthy tribute, an extended epilogue to the great book.

> The most stimulating and exciting objective experiences of Herman Melville's life came during the four years (1841–44) when he sailed the Pacific Ocean and wandered about its romantic isles. In three whaling vessels, two American and one Australian, he cruised for the great spermaceti whale of the South Seas.[4]

Cockayne's five-year voyage is a similar duration to that of a whaler, but more akin to Darwin's 1831 seasick journey taking place on board the *Pequod* rather than the *Beagle*. The many specimens found along the way by the artist are exhibited in a display comparable to the basement rooms of the Natural History Museum, where many a mystery and a monster may be found. *Dominion*'s ambiguous chimeras and filmed performances offer a dreamlike encounter with the whale. It is one which is explored through literary and also historical sources, citing the technological advancements the sperm whale has made possible, like submarine design and space exploration (as spermaceti does not freeze in extreme temperatures), to the most influential of all tales on *Moby-Dick*'s creation: Owen Chase's *Narrative of the Most Extraordinary and Distressing Shipwreck of the Whale-Ship Essex*. Cockayne is drawn to the idea that the famous sperm whale that stove the whale-ship Essex could have been a female protecting her young. In this reading, the many manly references are turned on their head by the idea that the book could have been called *Moby-Doll*!

> if, at my death, my executors, or more properly my creditors, find any precious MSS. in my desk, then here I prospectively ascribe all the honor and the glory to whaling; for a whale-ship was my Yale College and my Harvard.[5]

If the whale-ship would educate the subject and the literary and biblical references add allegory and symbolism, there's a suspicion that we are being lied to from the start. The famous opening line 'Call me Ishmael' holds derogatory terms. In Genesis, Ishmael was the son of the servant Hagar, fathered by her master Abraham and cast off after the birth of his legitimate son Isaac. Through the use of the term 'call me', Ishmael alludes to the fact that this may be an alias. Are we really being told to call our unwanted orphan a bastard, a traitor, a liar? He is our narrator, our storyteller, our educator and the novel's only human survivor. As he lays afloat the coffin made for Queequeg, shipwrecked and alone, and finds his resulting salvation in the shape of the *Rachel*, I can't help thinking about the most famous orphan of them all; Oliver Twist.

> The text is marked, as we shall see, by strikingly different modes of writing, as Dickens shifts rapidly between sentiment and sensation, storytelling and satire, murderous melodrama and dream.[6]

First published in 1838, *Oliver Twist* became an instant success for Dickens, an English writer of the same Herculean stature as America's Melville, but considered so in his own lifetime. Dickens' novel, like Melville's, is one that has taken many forms since its incarnation; a story that, like folklore, lives on through generations. I like to imagine Melville reading *Oliver Twist* and envisaging Ishmael through the child orphan, an unusual subject for nineteenth-century literature. Melville's very own orphan would take an exploratory journey into the unknown and meet people who would induce him to an unknown trade. On board the *Pequod*, he would assist in picking the pockets of the oceans for the good of the ships owners, Peleg and Bildad, his very own Fagins. The most striking similarity though, is the sadness felt at the abuse of each novel's title character.

> Like starlings the wind drives us
> into flight at the hour when
> the shadows fall. What remains to the last
> is the work undertaken[7]

Rachel's Orphan is not the full stop on *Dominion*, although it does signal the end of Cockayne's own whaling voyage. In all its manifestations *Dominion* has become a circular system. Like *Moby-Dick* it exists as a series of re-readable chapters, and like any great novel you are invited to turn from the last page back to its first. With the subject in hand you are once again greeted by no greater and recognisable negation, the most famous of introductions: Call me (add slight pause) Ishmael.

Source Notes

1   Herman Melville, 'Epilogue', *Moby-Dick; or, The Whale* (New York: Harper and Brothers, 1851).

2   Melville, 'Epilogue', *Moby-Dick*.

3   Melville, 'The Advocate', *Moby-Dick*.

4   Wilson Heflin, Herman Melville's Whaling Years (Nashville, TN: Vanderbilt University Press, 2004).

5   Melville, 'The Advocate', *Moby-Dick*.

6   Dr Ella Westland, 'Introduction' in Charles Dickins, *Oliver Twist* (Ware: Wordsworth Editions, 1995).

7   W. G. Sebald, *After Nature*, trans. Michael Hamburger (New York: Modern Library, 2002).

Jaw Stock. 2011. From the film *Rachel's Orphan*.

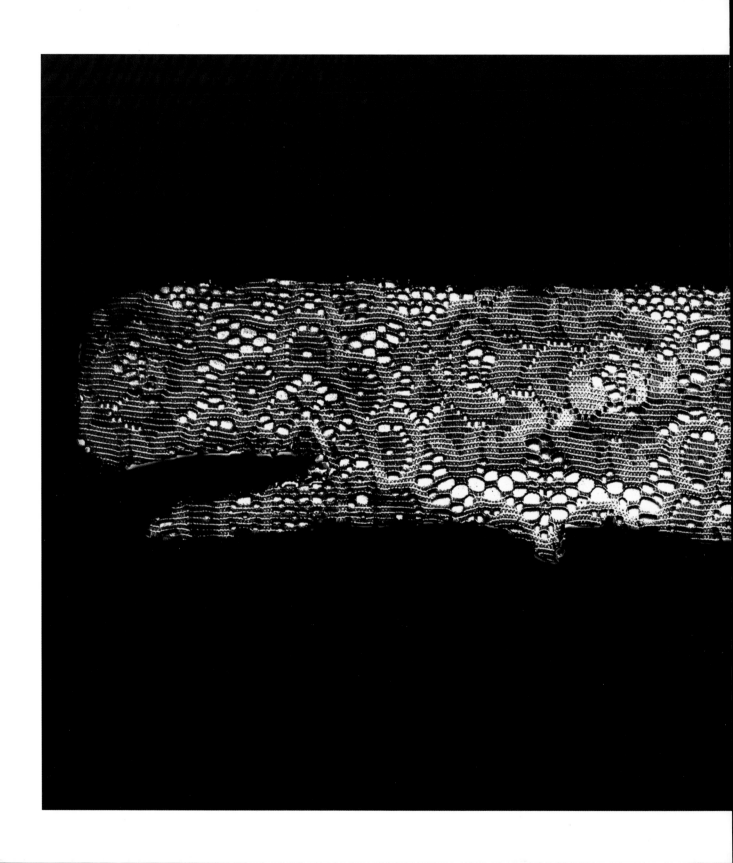

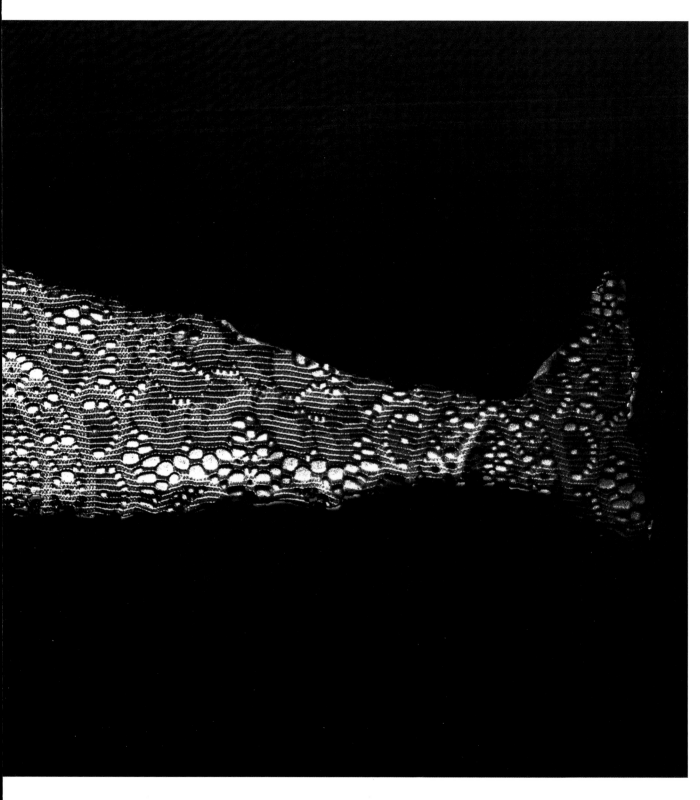

[ABOVE] *Land Lubber*. 2010. Boots, deerskin, jesmonite hooves.
[LEFT] *Fur UK*. 2010. Deer Skin.

LIST OF IMAGES
All images and photographs by Angela Cockayne unless stated

Angela Cockayne
Philip Hoare

Angela Cockayne, who lives and works in Bath, England, has exhibited widely. She is Reader in Interdisciplinary Arts Practice at Bath Spa University. Her work has recently toured with the House of Fairy Tales *Exquisite Trove*, an exhibition inspired by cabinets of curiosities or Wunderkammer. *Dominion* incorporates Cockayne's chimerical objects, part animal, part sculpture, with Philip Hoare's physical interaction with sperm whales. Using artwork and text thrown up by this new meeting of art, literature, music and science, the result is an aesthetic sermon on the state of the whale and the world. The film of the same name has been screened as part of the *Dark Monarch* exhibition, Tate St Ives 2009, Tate Liverpool. Liverpool 2010 and Cheltenham International Science Festival. She has work in private and public collections in UK, China and USA.

Every day nature offers us beautiful objects that we fail to appreciate because we see them only in the too-familiar context of their mundane roles. By taking them out of their usual contexts, Angela Cockayne makes us see them afresh, and in the process, creates an endearing whimsical bestiary all her own.
— Desmond Morris

Philip Hoare is the author of six works of non-fiction: *Serious Pleasures: The Life of Stephen Tennant* (1990) and *Noel Coward: A Biography* (1995), *Wilde's Last Stand: Decadence, Conspiracy, and the First World War* (1997), *Spike Island: The Memory of a Military Hospital* (2000), and *England's Lost Eden: Adventures in a Victorian Utopia* (2005). His latest book, *Leviathan or, The Whale*, won the 2009 BBC Samuel Johnson Prize for non-fiction. An experienced broadcaster, he presented the BBC 2 Arena film *The Hunt for Moby-Dick*, directed by Adam Low, and directed three films for BBC's *Whale Night* in 2008. His other work includes creative writing tutor, Hampshire County Council schools, 2005, creative writing tutor, HMP Albany, 2007-9, writer-in-residence, Ruskin College, Oxford, 2010, Leverhulme Artist-in-residence, The Marine Institute/ Plymouth University, 2011-12.

Nick Atkinson
Anthony Caleshu
Sarah Chapman

Michael Hall
Alexi Kirke
Ruth Leeney

Sam Richards
Andrew Sutton
Hal Whitehead

CONTRIBUTORS

Nick Atkinson is a composer and much of his work has involved writing music for film. He has collaborated with filmmaker Robert Fearns (Perfect Worlds, Beautiful Place and Off the Map), with poet Phillip Gross, and more recently with Angela Cockayne. Other compositions include Wintersnight for orchestra, commissioned with funding from the Arts Council. He has also written choral, instrumental, and chamber music. Nick studied at Bristol and Harvard Universities, and teaches at Bath Spa University, where he runs the BA Creative Arts course.

Anthony Caleshu is Associate Professor, Creative Writing and English, University of Plymouth and the author of a novella and two books of poems, most recently *Of Whales: in Print, in Paint, in Sea, in Stars, in Coin, in House, in Margins* (Salt, 2010). He is the winner of Boston Review's Poetry Contest (2010), for a suite of poems from his current work-in-progress, set in the Arctic. His critical study of the American poet James Tate is forthcoming in 2011 (Peter Lang).

Sarah Chapman is currently the Acting Director for Peninsula Arts, the public Arts programme for the University of Plymouth. This role involves her managing a broad cultural programme including Visual Arts, Performance, Film, Music and public lectures www.peninsula-arts.co.uk. As well as a curator Sarah has worked professionally as a book designer and photographer and has lectured on a number of University programmes in areas such as Media, Publishing and Digital Arts.

Michael Hall Born 1978, London UK. Lives and works in London. He is an artist, writer and the curator of the Parfitt Gallery, Croydon, London. Michael Hall completed a BA (Hons) Fine Art (First Class) at Croydon College in 2007 and an MA Printmaking at the Royal College of ArtIn 2009

Alexi Kirke is a composer based in the South-West of England who works across multiple platforms including the large-scale multimedia and acoustic works, and the creation of science-based algorithmic scores. He is composer-in-residence for the Plymouth Marine Institute Alexis holds two PhDs, one in Arts and one in Technology.

He has published articles on Algorithmic Composition and Performance. Alexis is a poet and critic who has written for publications such as Terrible Work, Oasis, Tremblestone (UK) and Transmog (US). He has also been invited to read at Glastonbury Festival, and was editor of the UK's first poetry webzine 'Brink'. Alexis' works have been performed on BBC Radio 3, the World Service, and at the Southbank; and he has been featured in Wired, Independent, Guardian, O Globo, Discovery News, New Scientist, Gramophone, and The Strad.

Ruth Leeney is a marine biologist, based in Falmouth, UK. She currently works as a post-doctoral researcher at the University of Plymouth. She has a PhD in Zoology from University College Dublin and has worked in such diverse places as Svalbard, The Gambia, Namibia and Cape Cod (USA). In over 10 years experience in research on marine mammals, her work has focused in particular on acoustic monitoring of dolphins and porpoises to provide an understanding of behaviour and habitat use. Her interest lies in research as a means of supporting conservation and management action for marine species and habitats.

More recently, Ruth has become interested in working in developing countries, providing local communities with outreach and education about the importance of knowing and protecting their marine fauna. She is also involved in the development of sustainable whale-watching practices in these places. She is, ultimately, concerned with the conflict between humankind and the oceans, and the reconciliation of that conflict into an appreciation and symbiosis.

Sam Richards is a composer and improviser whose music has been played in the UK and North America, and who has toured as an improviser, jazz pianist and folk singer. He has also written on John Cage and on Musical Democracy. His own scripts have been broadcast on national BBC Radio 3 and 4. He lectures at the University of Plymouth on the BA Music course.

Andrew Sutton is director of Nice Images (London, Madrid) and videographer/photographer for Survivors Fund (SURF UK), supporting victims of the Rwandan genocide. He is also co-founder of ECO2 marine research and education centre, Mikindani, Tanzania, and has made video guides for Sri Lankan, Jordanian and Emirates, filmed underwater sequences for the BBC, and worked alongside WWF (med + Indian Ocean), and the Sri Lankan Tourist Promotion Bureau.

Hal Whitehead is a University Research Professor in the Department of Biology at Dalhousie University in Canada. He holds a PhD in Zoology from Cambridge University. His research focuses on social organization and cultural transmission in the deep-water whales, especially sperm whales. Hal co-edited *Cetacean Societies: Field Studies of Whales and Dolphins;*(2000) and has written *Sperm Whales; Social Evolution in the Ocean*, (2003) and *Analyzing Animal Societies: Quantitative Methods for Vertebrate Social Analysis* (2008).

ACKNOWLEDGEMENTS

Bath Spa University would like to thank the following people and organisations:

Dr Hal Whitehead
Sarah Chapman
Simon Ible
Andrew Mouat
Jane Cullen
Paul Burtnyk
Kate Shorten
Monique Lemessurier
Emily Packer
David McErlane
Lloyd Russell
Dr Graham McLaren
Anna McLaren
Dorothy Cockayne
Robert Fearns
Jackson Fearns
Liberty Fearns
Raphaella Fearns
Jason Hobbs
Dr Alexis Kirke
Desmond Morris
Anthony Caleshu
Michael Hall
Catherine Haines
Dr Ruth Leeney
Sam Richards
Oona Grimes
Stephen Grimes's family
Matthew Robertson
Dr Jo Dahn
Viv Kenchington
Emmanuelle Ginn
John Taylor
Jon Warmington
Stephen Ricketts

Simon Butler
Tom Durnford
Mark Van De Woestyne
Steve Daniels
Jane Shaw
Maggie Powell
Jackie Puzey
Nick Atkinson
Jess Atkinson
Lorna Osbon
Andrew Sutton
Rachel Collingwood
Chris Jordan
Lone Star Studios
Prof. Ron George
Pradeep Sharma
Martin Thomas
WDCS
Penguin Books
Adam Low
Martin Rosenbaum and
Lone Star Productions
Michael Bracewell
Martin Atrill
Professor Stephen Sterling
Viktor Wynd
Kellie Hindmarch
Peninsular Arts
Plymouth University
The Leverhulme Trust
Jill Cotton and
Colman Getty PR

THE WHALE'S DOMINION

The whale abides in my dreams. It comes to me when I sleep, echo-locating my nightmares, rebuking me for her definition against the blue, blue-black descending into the profound. She will not allow me to close my eyes. And when I do, hooded phantoms swim into view, reverberating through my body. Oh the world, ah the whale.

Her kind were born at the beginning of time, before humans; it took fifty million years for the hunters to come, wanting light and oil in return for her flesh and blood. She swims in company, her knowledge reaches back into generations before the boats were built. Now the connexions have been severed, and her clicks and clangs echo unheard across oceans deafened by human noise. They made war out of her oily skin, incised and boiled and reduced her, but failed in their final solution. Ah the world, oh the whale.

Her genes spin into outer space, fill the minds of children, shape themselves. Hers is the largest brain of any living thing, yet we have no idea what she does with her grey matter, once discarded by the hunters, along with all the useless rest. Communicating in dialects we have yet to translate, she roams with her cetacean tribe like the elephant of the veldt, diving deeper than any other creature, into the devilish darkness and the domain of the giant squid, sometimes fearing that darkness, too.

Until yesterday, her only enemies were orca – whale killers of her own kind. Still she lives on as an imperial presence, forever shaped by her regal watery world, much as she shapes it in turn. And forever I am haunted by the procession of mothers she leads into my mind, as I close my eyes, unable to dispel her image in my head.

Oh the whale, ah the world.

Philip Hoare, 'Cassock and Dominion' film text.

Suckle. 2009. Teeth, denture wax, type-writer from Jamaica Inn.